FROM APE TO MAN

It began almost 2,000,000 years ago with the gradual disappearance of the great forests. Forced to adapt themselves to the new conditions of life on the plains, the earliest ancestors of man became hunters and meat eaters. Through gene mutation and natural selection, they lost their huge canine incisors, giving their brains space to enlarge. Slowly they became erect. Their hands became more precise and delicate. Man the toolmaker was born. As hunters they learned the value of cooperative activity. The exigencies of the hunt gave birth to human speech. The rutting season began to disappear in the women. It was replaced by almost continuous sexual receptivity. This led to monogomy and the establishment of stable family units. Slowly, over a period of hundreds of thousands of years, man as we know him finally emerged from the primordial darkness.

THE HUMAN REVOLUTION
by Ashley Montagu

BANTAM MATRIX EDITIONS

the human revolution

by Ashley Montagu

BANTAM BOOKS
NEW YORK/TORONTO/LONDON

THE HUMAN REVOLUTION

A Bantam Book/published by arrangement with
The World Publishing Company

● *PRINTING HISTORY*
World Publishing Company edition published September 1965
Bantam Matrix edition published December 1967

Bantam Books are published by Bantam Books, Inc., a subsidiary
of Grosset & Dunlap, Inc. Its trade-mark, consisting of the words
"Bantam Books" and the portrayal of a bantam, is registered in the
United States Patent Office and in other countries. Marca Registrada.
Bantam Books, Inc., 271 Madison Avenue, New York, N.Y. 10016.

PRINTED IN THE UNITED STATES OF AMERICA

To the Memory of
CHARLES GABRIEL SELIGMAN
Professor of Anthropology
in the University of London

PREFACE TO THE BANTAM EDITION

By "The Human Revolution" I mean the combination of innovations which brought about the changes which transformed an ape into a man. How these changes were brought about is the subject-matter of this book.

In this Bantam edition I have made many changes and a number of important additions, which I hope the reader will find helpful.

Princeton, N.J.   A.M.

FOREWORD

This book was delivered as a series of lectures at the National Science Foundation Summer Institute in Anthropology, at Flagstaff, Arizona, during the first sixteen days of July 1963. I am indebted to Dr. John H. Chilcott, Director of the Institute, and to Dr. Robert C. Euler, at the time Staff Anthropologist, as well as to my students, all high-school teachers, for making my stay at Flagstaff so memorably delightful.

To Dr. C. Loring Brace of the Department of Anthropology, University of California at Santa Barbara, and to Dr. J. Lawrence Angel of the Division of Anthropology, Smithsonian Institution, Washington, D.C., I owe thanks for the critical reading of the manuscript of this book. To Mary Ann Lively I owe thanks for her able typing of the manuscript. Finally, I am most grateful to Professor Raymond Dart for his ready help in supplying me with photographs of his important finds.

Princeton, N.J.   A.M.
1 May 1965

Contents

Illustrations

TABLES

A Moment in Time

The most critical "moment" in the history of humanity occurred when a creature that had never before done so picked up a stone, chipped off a flake or two to form a cutting edge, used it as a tool, and made other tools according to the same pattern from the same materials. That was the moment when a prehuman animal became a human animal and the human revolution began. Not only did that first of human beings make tools, but he made other tools after the same pattern and communicated the technique to his fellow creatures. In this way were the foundations of human culture initiated and established. It is the essence of the way of life of a group— that is, of its culture—that, having been created, it must be learned, it must be transmitted and perpetuated through learning. Culture, then, may be defined as the learned part of the environment. Learning is here defined as the increase in the strength of any act through repetition or training.

It is not that an ape suddenly turned into a man, for the process of evolution was quite gradual, an almost imperceptible merging from the behavior of an ape to that of a man. The direction of man's human evolution was already implicit in the behavioral potentialities of man's ancestors, as is clearly evident from the study of existing apes. The transition from ape to man was not revolutionary, but evolutionary. Yet, seen in the perspective of time, that change adds up to a genuine revolution, for it meant the adoption of a way of life so completely different from anything that had previously existed on earth that it constitutes, perhaps, almost as great a miracle as the emergence of living organisms from inorganic matter.

What distinguishes the human animal from all other animals is not the possession of culture, for almost all animals in some degree possess the elements of culture, but it is the capacity to make tools to a set and regular pattern, and the ability to use them for a variety of purposes. According to James Boswell (in his *Life of Samuel Johnson*), it was Benjamin Franklin who first defined man as a toolmaking animal.[1] This is an excellent definition, for while other animals may occasionally utilize or even modify material and use it as a tool for a specific purpose, it is not a common occurrence and such animals are not dependent, as men are, upon such elaborate tool-making for their continued survival.

There are some interesting cases of toolmaking among other animals, for example, the burrowing wasp *Ammophila* uses a small pebble as a hammer to pound down the soil over its nest of eggs. *Cactospiza,* one of Darwin's finches of the Galapagos Islands, uses a cactus spine to pick out insects from crevices in the bark of trees. The British greater spotted woodpecker uses clefts in tree trunks as vices into which it pushes pine cones, so that they may be held firmly while the birds pull out the seeds. The southern sea otter uses a stone, which it carries with it in the water, as an anvil on which to break the hard shells of the shellfish it feeds on. The Arnhem land hawk picks up smoldering sticks in its claws and drops them into a dry patch of grass, then waits with its companions for the exodus of frightened animals attempting to escape the fire, and falls upon them as they flee. Egyptian vultures pick up and throw stones at ostrich eggs with their beaks in order to break them open and feast upon the contents.

Undoubtedly these forms of behavior were contrived by ancestors of these animals, and have been continuously learned, transmitted, and perpetuated, in an unbroken tradition, by subsequent generations. These acts therefore constitute what we may loosely call cultural forms of behavior. As such, however, interesting as they are, they represent virtually the complete repertory of the inventions of these creatures. What makes the human animal unique is the uniqueness and complexity of his tools, not simply their number or variety, but their quality. The most important of those implements are not so much the material objects that have been transformed into tools, and the tools with which to make tools, but the organization of thoughts, the ideas, that enable the human animal to transform and to some extent control not only the world as he finds it, but also the world as he remakes it. *Homo faber,* man the maker, not only makes things but makes himself. Man is, indeed, the most remarkable of all his own creations. And he owes that creativeness virtually entirely to the fact that he is both a creator and a creature of ideas, a creature who manipulates his environment to suit his purposes by means of ideas, his concepts, his mental images, his abstractions—in short, his symbols.

The environment man makes for himself is created through his symbol-using ability, his capacity for abstraction. The man-made part of the environment is his culture—the binding of the past to work upon the present to modify and control the future. It is the ability to intellectualize and physically experience and communicate certain forms of behavior in a complex and successful manner. This distinguishes man from all other creatures on this earth. Man is the toolmaking animal, and he is so only because he is the symbol-using animal. The most important of all his tools are his symbols. The symbols, the ideas, are created in the mind, i.e., conceptualized. Such constructs have no counterpart in the external world, but the human animal learns not only to create them, but to project them upon the external world, and there transform them into reality. And this the human animal can do because he is a symbol maker, *Homo symbolicus*.

> The idea is that which already exists, but has no form.
> It is art not yet realized.
> The idea is a point of departure.
> The lifting of a veil's edge.
> A first faint stirring,
> Or like the leap of a violin
> In a moment of despairing gloom.[2]

A symbol as used here is an abstraction or organization of ideas which represents something which has no external reality, something having no external reality in that it occurs in the mind, and though experienced there constitutes no part of the external world, but remains essentially part of the human world. Symbols are of functional value only. Signals differ from symbols in belonging more strictly to the physical world, and the meanings they convey are derived from the physical form they take in the external world. Most of the communication between animals is of the signaling variety. It is man alone who communicates virtually exclusively through symbols.

Many animals are capable of some symbol usage, and there can be no doubt that man's protohuman ancestors were capable of some symbol usage long before any of them made a tool out of a material object. The contemporary great apes—orangutan, chimpanzee, and gorilla—are capable of symbol usage to a limited degree, and under challenging conditions sometimes exhibit quite remarkable innovatory behavior. For example, a chimpanzee will place box upon box and climb the structure so built in order to reach a bunch of bananas. This ape has also been observed to insert one stick into another

to make a pole with which to reach a bunch of bananas.
Chimpanzees and orang-utans will fold straw into a firm
implement with which to reach desired objects. Under natural
conditions chimpanzees have been observed to pick a straw
or dried stem of grass and poke this carefully down the hole
in a termite heap. The termites bite the straw and hang on to
it; the chimpanzee is aware of this, gently withdraws the stem,
and licks off the adhering victims with relish. Miss Jane Goodall, a young English field observer, has seen chimpanzees
anticipate the event by breaking off a twig from a tree, strip-
ping it of leaves and side stems, and going from one termite
hill to another, sedulously searching for a meal.[3] If a tool is
an object modified or changed in order to act upon something
else, then quite clearly the chimpanzee is not only a rudimentary toolmaker, but capable of conceptualizing the use of a
simple tool for an immediately future purpose.

As we should expect, there exists no great chasm between
the rudimentary tool-modifying activity of the ape and the
toolmaking of the earliest men—the continuum is, in fact,
unbroken. The difference, as in so much else, between the
toolmaking of the ape and the toolmaking of man lies in the
increase in complexity of man's tools.

The living great apes are collateral but not linear relations
of man. The stock ancestral to both the great apes and to the
line which eventually led to man is represented by the fossil
genus known as *Dryopithecus*. *Dryopithecus* originated in the
Miocene epoch, some 28 million years ago (see Table I).
Originating from *Dryopithecus* or possibly from the African
ape *Proconsul* of the same age (see p. 11), the line which led
to the great apes and the line which ultimately gave rise to
man have pursued their evolutionary histories quite separately
for at least 25 million years. In spite of the fact that the great

---

The estimated number of millions of years in the fourth column for the
Tertiary period is based upon a combination of paleontological data,
with specific reference to the evolution of the horse from *Hyracotherium*
to *Equus*, and the evidence of geology and radioactivity. The figures for
the preceding periods are largely based on the uranium transformation
method. When uranium and lead occur together in a fragment of rock
otherwise free from these elements, it may generally be safely assumed
that the lead represents "decomposed" or transformed uranium. It is
known that 1,000,000 grams of uranium yield 1/7600 grams of lead a
year. Hence the age of such rocks can be determined from the proportions of these elements which they contain, thus:

$$\text{Age of rock} = \frac{\text{Weight of Lead}}{\text{Weight of Uranium}} \times 7600 \text{ million years}$$

TABLE I
GEOLOGICAL TIME SCALE OF THE APPEARANCE OF VARIOUS REPRESENTATIVE
FORMS OF LIFE

Era	Period	Epoch	Millions of years since the beginning of each epoch	Forms of life
CENOZOIC The Age of Mammals	Quaternary	Recent	1/40	Man, the slave and master.
		Pleistocene	2	*Australopithecus, Pithecanthropus, Sinanthropus, Swanscombe, Homo sapiens.*
	Tertiary	Pliocene	12	*Kenyapithecus.* First men probably appeared during the latter part of this epoch.
		Miocene	28	Appearance of true anthropoid apes. *Dryopithecus, Sivapithecus, Proconsul.*
		Oligocene	39	Primitive anthropoid apes appear such as *Propliopithecus.*
		Eocene	58	Spread of modern mammals. Tarsiers.
		Paleocene	75	Appearance of insectivorous pre-primates and earliest primates, primitive lemuroids and tarsioids.
MESOZOIC The Age of Reptiles	Secondary	Cretaceous	135	Rise of archaic mammals and birds. Extinction of dinosaurs, pterodactyls, and toothed birds. Insectivores.
		Jurassic	165	Spread of primitive mammals and pterodactyls, rise of toothed birds.
		Triassic	205	Rise of dinosaurs, pterodactyls, and primitive mammals.
PALEOZOIC The Age of Ancient Life		Permian	230	Spread of amphibians and insects. Extinction of trilobites.
		Carboniferous	255	Primitive reptiles, insects, spiders. Great forests of ferns and mosses.
		Devonian	325	Rise of fishes and amphibians. Spreading of forests.
		Silurian	360	Rise of ostracoderms, sea-scorpions (Eurypterids). First land plants.
		Ordovician	425	First primitive fishes, the ostracoderms.
		Cambrian	505	Still no land-life known, trilobites, mollusks, brachiopods.
PROTEROZOIC			925	Sponges, protozoöns, diatoms, and protophyta, and other commencing complex forms of life developed during this era.
ARCHEOZOIC			1,500	Probably simple unicellular sea-dwelling forms.

apes are only our distant collateral relations, we can learn a good deal about the way of life of our prehuman ancestors from the study of the apes in their natural habitats. Indeed, without such a study it would be quite impossible to understand the nature of the conditions that made the human revolution possible.

The Order of Primates

The living order of mammals known as the Primates consists of the lemurs, lorises, tarsiers, New World monkeys, Old World monkeys, gibbons, orang-utan, chimpanzee, gorilla, and man. With few exceptions these are inhabitants of the tropical and neotropical parts of the world, and they are largely forest dwellers. The gibbon and the orang-utan are tree dwellers. The chimpanzee and the gorilla spend most of their time on the ground, retiring at night to the lower branches of trees to sleep in roughly built nests. Populations in the great ape bands are small, rarely exceeding and seldom reaching forty individuals. All primates, with the exception of man, are predominantly vegetarian (herbivorous), occasionally eating the eggs of birds, larvae, some insects, birds, and sometimes, as among baboons and chimpanzees, larger animals.

In their various forms, the primates are perfectly adapted to their forest environments. There can be very little doubt that the prehuman ancestors of man were, like the chimpanzee and the gorilla, ground-dwelling inhabitants of the forest. It is unlikely that they were arboreal forms. A forest environment is not a very challenging one because it supplies a ready-made abundance of food to the animals living in it. The table is, as it were, laid. All one needs to do in order to eat is to reach for the food that is already there. What is therefore mostly required in order to meet the challenges, such as they are, presented by the forest environment, is the necessary physical equipment. For this purpose, well-developed teeth, especially upper and lower canines, are desirable. For non-grazing or nonbrowsing herbivorous animals large canines are invaluable because they make easy the shredding of the hard outer coverings of many plants, particularly of saplings. Under natural conditions one may observe apes draw young saplings toward them and effectively shred the bark from them with their canines. Such a feat would be difficult without large canines. It is this shredding, not combat or protection, which is the principal function of large canines. Large canine teeth are useful in defense against predators, but their primary function is not as weapons but to serve to make available plant foods that would otherwise have to be bypassed. Defense against predators is a purely secondary function that such teeth may perform. As Schultz has pointed out, protection is most efficiently provided by the combined alertness and keen vision of the organized social group. "The long canines of adult monkeys and apes are not very dependable weapons, since they become broken, abscessed, or even lost, especially after the enamel has partly worn off, far more frequently than they do in carnivores."[4]

Combat is infrequent among the great apes, as between themselves and as between themselves and other animals. Since the great apes are mainly herbivorous, they are unlikely, with the exception of the chimpanzee, to seek out other animals for food. In an age when struggle, conflict, war, and violence were congenial to the temper of the times, large canine teeth were interpreted as evidence of the combative nature of the great apes—a libel upon these creatures which is the very opposite of the truth, for under natural conditions they are the most amiable of creatures, and avoid conflict of any kind with other animals. With the exception of the Gombe chimpanzee, who will kill and eat monkeys, bucks, and pigs, they do not attack other creatures unless violently provoked.[3, 5, 6] This is an important fact to underscore, for there has been a considerable amount of mythology bequeathed to us concerning the behavior of these creatures, designed not to set out the facts but, at least in part, to justify the ways of man toward apes. The rationalization is that "Nature" red in tooth and claw shrieks against the creed of man. The reverse is the truth for it is man who is red in tooth and claw and who shrieks against the creed of Nature.[7]

The mythology we have inherited concerning the nature of "Nature" makes it possible to fit the picture of man's evolution into the framework of "the warfare of Nature" of which Darwin and the Darwinists wrote. In such muscular Darwinian works it is still the custom to portray man's prehuman ancestors as inhuman ferocious beasts. The course of man's evolution is pictured as the gradual subjugation of this seething violence under the growing influence of civilization. Again, this is the very opposite of the truth. The fact is that as man has advanced in civilization he has become increasingly, not less, violent and warlike. The violences that have been attributed to his original nature have, in fact, been acquired predominantly within the relatively recent period of man's cultural evolution. In our own time most of us have grown so accustomed to the life of each for himself that it is difficult for us to understand that for the greater part of man's history every man of necessity lived a life of involvement in the welfare of his fellows. If we have misinterpreted the life of prehistoric man and his prehuman ancestors through the distorting glass of our modern prejudices, there no longer remains any reason why we should continue to do so. The important thing for us is not to deny our prejudices and prejudgments, but to acknowledge them, and to consider the evidence concerning the nature of our prehuman ancestors in the light of the facts.

The great apes usually give birth to a single newborn. The gestation period is roughly the same in great apes and in man: 39 weeks in the orang-utan; 33 weeks in the chimpanzee; 36 weeks in the gorilla; and 38 weeks in man. Ape young mature more rapidly than human young, so that by the age of six months young apes are very well able to manage for themselves. At all ages there are generally more females present in an ape band than there are males. Since reproductive age is reached by about eight to nine years and the average duration of life is about forty years, three generations, and sometimes four, may coexist in ape bands. Intervals between the birth of infants are usually from three to four and a half years. As in man, mortality is highest for infants during the first year of life, death usually resulting from disease. Maternal care of the young is devoted, continuous, and tender, and discrimination of one's own offspring from the offspring of others is clear and unequivocal, on the part at least of the mother. Breast feeding usually lasts about twelve months; then weaning is gradually begun. Solid food is ingested by three months, and considerable amounts of vegetation are eaten by five months.

Dominance relationships, in which one individual exerts his precedence and power over another, usually exist between males, largely based on age and body power. Every band has a leader, who is usually an older individual, wise in the ways of his group. Family life among the apes is most intriguing. In the mountain gorilla, for example, the bands vary in size from five to twenty-five individuals. In the first few months after birth the babies are carried close to their mother's breasts; as they grow older they migrate to her back and travel there until 'they are about two and one-half years old. They continue to sleep at their mother's side sometimes until they are three or four years old. Both females and infants like to sit near the dominant male. The latter will accept baby-sitting duties and will freely permit several lively infants to climb all over him and hitch rides on his back. The dominant male, then, stands as it were in the relation of spouse to the females who have become mothers, and as father in relation to the young of the females, without, of course, any necessary explicit recognition of the one role or the other. And certainly he is their chief protector. The dominant male does not, nor do any of the other males, provide food for the females or for the young. This is done by the mothers, for it is upon them that virtually the entire burden of caring for the young falls, a burden that usually lasts some three or four years.

Living under such conditions in the sheltered environment of the forest, wandering over a limited range of territory, never settled permanently in one place, these animals face challenges to survival that are not very great. All that is required, in addition to the physical equipment necessary to meet the pressures of the environment, is little more than the limited range of responses learned from one's elders. Neither reaction nor response has any pressure put upon it by the environment for improvement or modification; the narrow range of challenges with which these animals are confronted is fully met by their equally limited range of reaction and response. This is not to say that apes or even monkeys are born with nothing more than an instinctual system which limits them to the appropriate reactions to the environment. The fact is their instinctual equipment is not highly developed, and that they have to learn most of their responses to the environment in much the same way human beings do. The difference lies principally in the fact that the hereditary constitution, the genotype, of these nonhuman primates places far greater limits upon what they are capable of learning than does the hereditary constitution of man.

As between the "lower" animals and man a gradual transition has occurred—from dominance of instincts and comparatively limited learning capacities to the shedding of instincts and the dominance of the capacity to learn, especially in determining social behavior. Capacities, potentialities, can be transformed into abilities only insofar as the limits of those capacities allow and the opportunities are afforded for their development. In the forest environment it is possible for millions of years to pass with little or no change in the behavioral system developing; for the simple reason that where the environment is unchanging, the need for change in the behavioral system, which is perfectly adapted to it, does not arise. Specialized for life in the forest, the apes have become admirably adapted to it.

Though not as specialized, the ancestors of the precursors of man were probably not very different in their ways of life from those of the living great apes. What were those creatures like? Fortunately we are in a position to do more than speculate in order to answer that question, for there exist several fossil forms which provide us with some indication of what the forerunners of the ancestors of man were like.

The Dryopithecines—The Ancestral Stock That Led to the Great Apes and to Man

The stock that almost certainly gave rise on the one hand to the line that led to the great apes, and on the other to the line that led to man, is known as *Dryopithecus*, of the subfamily Dryopithecinae of the superfamily Hominoidea (which includes the great apes and man, living and fossil, but excludes the monkeys). The dryopithecines are represented by two main series, African and Indian. The fragmentary fossil remains of well over five hundred specimens of *Dryopithecus* have been discovered over a wide geographic range extending from Africa to Europe and India. The precursors of the great apes and man were, therefore, already widely ranging forms in the Miocene epoch, some 25 million years ago, for it is from that epoch that most dryopithecine remains have been recovered. The series of dryopithecines from the Siwalik Hills of India and Pakistan do not differ significantly from the series of dryopithecines recovered from East Africa on Rusinga Island and at Fort Ternan. There are no real differences between *Sivapithecus indicus* from the Siwaliks and *Proconsul major* from Rusinga Island. Dr. Elwyn Simon, who has recently restudied these specimens, in addition can find no difference between the dryopithecine *Ramapithecus brevirostris* from the Siwaliks and the recently discovered *Kenyapithecus wickeri* (see below). The first two forms may well belong to the same species, as may the two latter forms (though to a different one from the two preceding forms). However this may be, it is clear that the stock ancestral to the great apes and man was neither small in number nor sedentary in its habits, for it appears to have been widely distributed over the eastern hemisphere.

Some of the best preserved dryopithecines are from East Africa, and so we shall briefly describe them, for they are important to our story.

An interesting dryopithecine dates from the Middle or Late Miocene epoch, some 16 or more million years ago. This is the genus of apelike creatures known as *Proconsul*. The genus *Proconsul* is known from nine localities in Kenya Colony, and from Kapak in northeastern Uganda. Three species have been identified, *Proconsul africanus, Proconsul major,* and *Proconsul nyanzae. Proconsul* had an apelike skull with large canine teeth, a narrow jaw, a forward convergence of the tooth rows, a small brain, and a quadrupedal gait (Figs. 1 and 2). If he ever stood erectly, *Proconsul* did not exceed three feet in height. The mammalian remains found in association with *Proconsul* indicate that he lived in an open savanna country, bordering on lakes with some forest galleries, that is to say, with some narrow-ranged forest regions still remaining. A savanna is an open grassland characterized by scattered trees and low-growing and intermittent vegetation. The limb bones of *Proconsul* indicate that he could well have lived in the trees, that his ancestors undoubtedly did so, but that owing to deforestation of large areas of the territory in which those ancestors had originally lived, *Proconsul* had to some extent adjusted to a life on the savanna.

There is good evidence—geological, botanical, climatological, and ecological—that beginning in the Lower Miocene, Africa, from its southernmost tip to the equator, was subject to periodic changes in rainfall. With the withdrawal of the rain, there were long, dry desiccated periods during which the forested regions suffered and in large part turned into savannas. These dry periods were followed by wet periods, called pluvials. Five dry non-pluvial periods have been established as having occurred in Africa during the course of man's evolution. *Proconsul,* in this connection, is of considerable

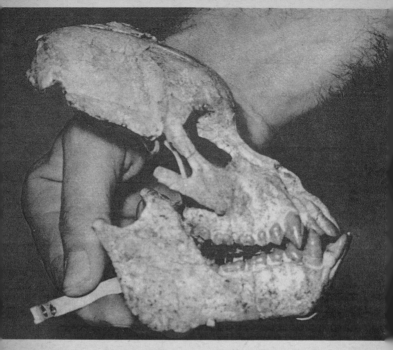

FIG. 1   Skull of *Proconsul africanus*. (*Courtesy of the National Geographic Society.*)

interest to us, because he lived in an earlier period of climatic change in response to which he may have undergone modifications which took his descendants several steps further toward the line of man. In any event, were this not so, he would still be of the greatest interest to us because he shows us something of what an unspecialized ape looked like, one which could well have been ancestral on the one hand to the living apes and on the other to man; the living apes having specialized to meet the challenges of the forest environment, the manlike forms specialized in remaining unspecialized, and adaptable, at least some of them, to whatever changes were rung in on them.

Proconsul has a well-rounded frontal bone without the overhanging eyebrow ridges of the chimpanzee and gorilla; he does not have an "internal chin," the simian shelf which binds the two halves of the mandible together; his molar teeth are small.

FIG. 2 How *Proconsul nyanzae* may have appeared. (*From a painting by Maurice Wilson; courtesy of the British Museum* [*Natural History*].)

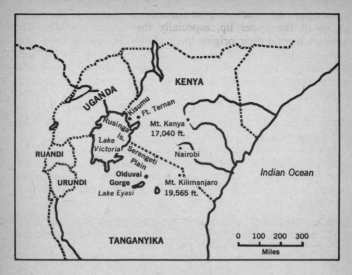

FIG. 3   Olduvai Gorge and Fort Ternan in East Africa. (*Courtesy of the National Geographic Society.*)

He is a primitive, unspecialized ape, and as such he could well constitute a progenitor of the ancestors of man.

Kenyapithecus wickeri

In 1962 Mr. Helson Mukuri, senior field assistant to Dr. L. S. B. Leakey, discovered an advanced proconsulid at the base of the Pliocene, dating back some 14 million years. The find was made at Fort Ternan, Kenya (Fig. 3). The age of the specimen was determined by the potassium-argon method from samples of the overlying deposits. *Kenyapithecus wickeri* is represented by a portion of the left side of the upper jaw with the canine tooth, the root of the first premolar, and the complete second premolar and first and second molars. The canine is quite reduced (Fig. 4), and the remaining teeth are quite manlike. The premaxillary diastema or simian gap, the space on each side of the upper jaw which separates the lateral incisor from the canine, is not present. There is a depression, the canine fossa, in the jaw above the root of the canine tooth. This is a trait limited to man. The canine fossa gives origin to muscles whose function is control of the movements of the upper lip, especially the lateral portions. The muscles having their origins in or above the canine fossa provide the upper lip and corner of the mouth with the mobility they require for speech. A similar fossa sometimes is present in the lower jaw, associated with similarly functioning muscles regulating the movements of the lower lip. The mandibular "canine fossa" is also unique to man. Both fossae are the result of the relative decrease in tooth size as compared with the supporting bone.

No tools were found associated with *Kenyapithecus*. Almost certainly, *Kenyapithecus* represents an early manlike ape that had taken a number of significant steps in the proto-hominid direction. It is quite evident that *Kenyapithecus* is

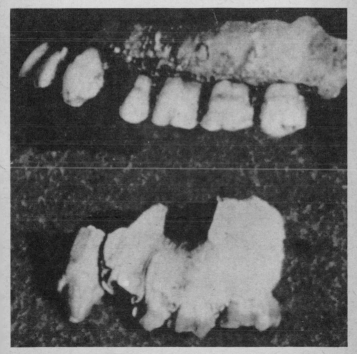

FIG. 4 Portion of the left side of the upper jaw of *Kenyapithecus wickeri* (below) compared with that of a modern man. (*Courtesy of the National Geographic Society.*)

already preadapted, that is to say, already endowed with the
physical traits necessary for speech. But *Kenyapithecus* almost
certainly did not have the necessary development of the brain,
and almost equally certainly was subject to none of the pressures that would have led to the development of speech. What
is most illuminating is that *Kenyapithecus* should exhibit these
morphological variations in the direction of man so early in
the Pliocene. This strongly suggests that evolution in the direction of man probably occurred much earlier than we have in
the past been inclined to believe, and that the evolution of
man extends over a much longer period than was formerly
thought possible. These suggestions are lent further support by
the find next to be discussed.

Oreopithecus bambolii

An early form that had already developed many manlike traits
is represented by a fossil primate first discovered in the 1860's
in the lignite of Montebamboli, in the province of Grosseto in
northern Italy. For many years, this form, known as *Oreopithecus bambolii,* was relegated to the status of an Old World
monkey-like form (Fig. 5). Re-examination of the original
fossil remains, with others since recovered, shows that this
Lower Pliocene form, about 10 million years old, had developed a considerable number of manlike traits. The teeth
are small, the simian gap is absent as in man, the canine teeth
are small, the upper and lower incisor teeth are implanted
steeply in the jaws (unlike the rather more forward, slantwise
projection of these teeth in the apes). The face is short, and
straighter (orthognathic) than in the apes; the chin region of
the lower jaw is steep and not slanted as in the apes; the
lumbar vertebrae are relatively large and robust; and finally,
the pelvis possesses a number of manlike features indicating
that *Oreopithecus* was capable of bipedal progression. The
fact, however, that his arms were appreciably longer than his
legs, a condition peculiar to habitual brachiators (that is,
animals that habitually progress through the trees by overarm
swinging), suggests that *Oreopithecus* was a brachiator. It is
generally agreed that *Oreopithecus* was ancestral neither to
the great apes nor to man, and represents an evolutionary side-
branch that produced no offshoots.

Thus the primitive ape *Proconsul* and the more advanced
ape *Kenyapithecus,* as well as *Oreopithecus,* give us some idea
of the kind of primate forms that developed in the line leading

FIG. 5 Reconstruction of the skeleton of *Oreopithecus bambolii*. (*Courtesy of* SCIENTIFIC AMERICAN.)

to the ancestors of man. The important thing for us to note is that these forms remained relatively unspecialized. That is to say, they did not follow a special line of development, but retained a generalized plasticity, which enabled them to adjust to a multiplicity of changing conditions.

The prehuman ancestors of man, we may be certain, retained these traits of generalized plasticity, without specialization. When changing environments presented them with new and challenging demands, they were not so far fixed in specialization as to be unable to make the necessary responses. Having retained their primitive malleability, and, indeed, having already moved in a direction not far removed from the possibilities of humanity, they were ready for the change, preadapted, as it were, to give the appropriate answer to the questions they were to be asked, to the challenges with which they were to be confronted.

The Challenges of the New Environment

The apelike creatures that had evolved in Africa would probably have remained apelike had it not been, as we have already
pointed out, for the development of climatic changes which
presented them with a variety of challenges requiring certain
kinds of responses. Without those challenges and responses
there would have been no man. For the organization of the
responses to these challenges is essentially what man is. Those
challenges were ecological, that is, they involved a dynamic
relation between these prehuman forms and the environmental
conditions in which they found themselves. The conditions
which go to make up the ecological pattern or ecosystem, the
game, the vegetation, the water supply, are all dependent upon
the climate. Every living organism must adjust to the environment determined by the climate in which it finds itself, or
succumb to it.

During that period of time which is sometimes called the
Plio-Pleistocene boundary, that is to say, the period toward
the end of the Pliocene and the period including the beginning of the Pleistocene, some two million years ago, our preadapted, largely bipedal, prehuman ancestors were already
flourishing in small numbers in Africa below the equator, for
the evolution of man's prehuman ancestors undoubtedly occurred during the Pliocene. Toward the end of the Pliocene
and the beginning of the Pleistocene, as already stated, a great
part of Africa south of the Sahara had gradually become de-
forested as a result of the reduction in the rainfall. The semi-
arid grassland savannas into which the woodlands were in this
way transformed presented the manlike apes that once lived
in the forests with entirely new ecological challenges. It is not
that they abandoned the forest, but that the forest abandoned
them—a change to which they were forced to adjust or perish.

The change from woodlands to savanna occurred gradually
over a considerable period of time, running into many hundreds of thousands of years. Adjustment to the new conditions of life would have been equally gradual and slow.

In the forest the apes are food gatherers, and eat what they
gather on the spot. It is probable that man's prehuman ancestors continued this way of life wherever they could on the
savannas. We have fairly good evidence of this, and shall refer
to it in the proper place. In regions, however, in which the

vegetation was insufficient to maintain life by food gathering, the means of livelihood would, under pressure of the ecological conditions, have to be enlarged. From the gathering of plant foods to the gathering of small, slow-moving animals, young birds before they are fledged in the nest, infant and other easily secured animals, is but a step, for, as we have seen, the baboon and the chimpanzee occasionally make a meal of other animals. With the habitual assumption of such an extended dietary these manlike apes became omnivores, that is to say, anything they could find that was edible they ate. This was a giant, a revolutionary, step, for it was the first time it had been made a regular practice by any member of the large order of mammals to which this creature belonged. Indeed, there are very few species of animals who have at any time adventured such a step. It is the first of the innovations in their mode of life that led, in a multiplicity of ways, to the development of humanity in what were manlike apes and who thereby became apelike men.

Consider a few of the consequences of the adoption of an omnivorous diet. By becoming an omnivore, an animal increases its capacity for survival in all environments immeasurably. An omnivore can eat and digest virtually everything that is edible or that it can render so. This is one of the principal reasons why the brown rat and man have become the most widespread of all the mammals of the earth, and possibly why (the cynic may remark) they have so much in common. As a behavioral response to the challenge of the environment the adoption of an omnivorous diet is of the highest adaptive value. Among other things, it extends the range of experience, and therefore the range of behavior. For this reason carnivores and omnivores generally are characterized by a far wider repertory of behavior patterns than herbivores. Herbivores eat foods that have their roots fixed in the earth, and have merely to approach and eat thereof. Meat eaters eat foods that have their roots in their stomachs, so to speak, and are highly mobile. Those foods have to be run down and caught before they can be consumed. This necessitates the solution of all sorts of problems in all sorts of special ways—challenges with which herbivores are never faced—and hence makes special demands upon the adaptive capacities of the creatures engaged in such a mode of life. This is a subject to which we shall return shortly, for it is of the first order of importance for an understanding of the manner in which a group of prehuman or protohuman manlike apes became a group of ape-like men—men in the true sense of that word, and men not one whit the less for looking more apelike than men subsequently came to look.

The revolutionary change from a forest-living herbivorous way of life to embrace animal gathering on the open savannas probably lasted a considerable time, and very likely occurred toward the end of the Pliocene. The precursors of man were probably tool users and tool modifiers, but not yet toolmakers. In the course of time, however, their new omnivorous way of life led directly to the invention of toolmaking. Following upon the adoption of the bipedal erect posture (pp. 37, 138–143), it would often have been the case that in the foraging for infant and young animals, or slow-moving ones, some of the young prey would attempt to escape. Stones would have been thrown at them in the endeavor to bring them down. Such stones would sometimes break and flake, leaving sharp edges. These would make good knives with which to skin the young animals, and the fact that an unprepared stone could be flaked deliberately to form a cutting tool would lead to a simple next step. "A simple next step." But what a step! That first step constituted no less than the birth of the first industrial revolution, for it was not merely the invention of toolmaking that was involved, but its transmission and perpetuation as an industrial tradition. This was a cultural revolution, for it constituted a revolution in the way of life, by means of which the power of both the individual and the group was greatly extended mechanically, physically, and, quite as importantly, psychologically. It was one thing to find objects that could be used as tools; it was quite another to find out how to *create* tools. A variety of objects were undoubtedly found to be serviceable as tools by man's immediate ancestors, and discarded as soon as they had served their purpose. This is a very different thing from discovering, from *finding out,* how to make such tools, and to make them thereafter according to a set pattern handed down by tradition. Man is the creature that turns accidents into opportunities. He is the most accomplished of all opportunists.

With the invention and establishment of the toolmaking tradition the man-apes that initiated it became men, primitive men certainly, but men unequivocally by the measure of our definition of man as the toolmaking animal who has become continuously dependent on tools for survival.[8]

Teeth, hands, fists, and fingernails are useful, but there are many things a stone tool can do much more effectively than these parts of one's anatomy. Stone tools are harder, stronger, more powerful, sharper, faster, and more efficient in their performance than the natural equipment with which primates are endowed. Furthermore, in one simple tool can be combined all the functions of the natural endowment of the tool-like parts of the body. A simple stone tool can cut, carve, pound, hammer, pierce, shred, scrape, slice, and, what is more, it can also serve as an implement to bring down a quarry at a distance. Because they become the extensions not only of the body but also of the mind, tools embody the versatility of their makers. They arc at the bidding of their makers in a multiplicity of ways.

With reference to throwing stones at a quarry at a distance in order to bring it down, it should be understood that throwing as such was not an innovation of the man-apes, but a continuation and extension of a form of behavior which is common to many monkeys, who will throw whatever is available, including their own feces, at objects of their displeasure. In the absence of such objects chimpanzees in captivity will frequently spit or urinate at their targets. They are usually excellent shots. However, prior to the development of an omnivorous diet, it is unlikely that any primate resorted to throwing as a means of securing another animal.

Toolmaking constitutes a response to the environment which is of the highest adaptive value, in that it greatly increases the chances of survival. It is a form of behavior which undoubtedly arose as an adaptive response to the challenges of life on the savannas, especially in response to the assumption of the habit of meat eating.

The origin of toolmaking has a long history, and, as Napier has pointed out, normal cultural toolmaking must have been preceded by ad hoc toolmaking, and even earlier by tool modifying. Wood, bone, and stone provided the materials from which tools must have been made on many occasions, and Napier suggests that the persistence of the tradition or new-fangled "craze" may have come about only with the evolution of speech and language. Cultural toolmaking he regards as a culminating event in a continuum of manual activity perhaps beginning as early as the Miocene and proceeding along some such lines as these:

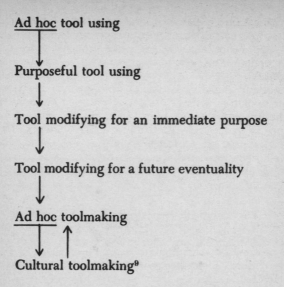

<u>Ad hoc</u> tool using

↓

Purposeful tool using

↓

Tool modifying for an immediate purpose

↓

Tool modifying for a future eventuality

↓

<u>Ad hoc</u> toolmaking

↓   ↑

Cultural toolmaking[9]

Apes must have a visible reward usually before they will make a tool, although we have seen that chimpanzees are capable of anticipatory behavior, and will prepare a stick before going "fishing" for termites. So that man is not alone in visualizing, in abstractly conceiving of the usefulness of shaping an object into a tool for use on a future occasion, without the immediate presence of the rewarding incentive. He is unique only in the extent to which he engages in such anticipatory abstraction. A deliberately fashioned tool becomes in itself a plan for the future. The ape may upon occasion make a tool in anticipation of future use, but he seldom does so, and he does not make such cultural tools as implements upon which he is continuously dependent for survival, as man does. It is not that the ape makes no plans for the future. It is clear that in a rudimentary sort of way he does so, but what is also clear is that he lives mostly in the immediate present. The ape concretely perceives what requires to be done. Man abstractly conceives of a tool, even in the absence of the conditions for which the use of tools may be required, and imposes the model he has in his mind upon the formless raw material. Using symbols as his tools, he endows the formless and the functionless with form and function. Tools represent the application of past experience by their present makers to affect the future. That is the essence of a cultural activity. Apes do not possess this capacity to any but the most limited extent and, hence, have the most rudimentary cultural capacities, and almost certainly for the same reason lack the capacity for speech.

Important as the invention of tools was in the history of human evolution, it is not so much the tools themselves that are the important things as what their invention signified: an advance in intelligence. At this juncture it should perhaps be made clear that the customary manner of describing the gap in intelligence which exists between the apes and man as being "vast" is in error. There does not in fact exist a "vast gap" between the intelligence of apes and man. This way of phrasing the matter is merely a manner of speaking, which obscures the fact that, as Professor Harry Harlow has put it: "The probability is that a relatively small intellectual gain by man over the anthropoid apes would make possible the development of symbolic language and also culture."[10] The difference in the cultural achievements between men and apes is very considerable indeed, but that difference, great as it is, is itself almost certainly due to a relatively small number of gene differences as between the apes and man. The gap which separates the apes and man is genetically comparatively small; the gap which separates them culturally is very large indeed. The suggestion is that small genetic differences in the one group, by their absence or different molecular structure, limit the development of the range of possible responses to the environment along certain lines, whereas in the other group, because of a slightly different genetic constitution the possibility of a much larger range of responses becomes feasible.

It is reasonable to suppose that there probably were no vast changes in the genetic constitution involved in the transformation from ape-man, to man-ape, to man. Those genetic changes were almost certainly very slight ones, but slight as they may have been they were of a momentous kind, for they provided the genetic basis for the ability to respond to the challenges of the environment with just that modicum of difference in solving problems that ultimately made the difference between ape and man. That advance in behavior, problem-solving behavior, we call *intelligence*. Toolmaking is a material token of intelligence. That is what toolmaking tells us there had been a significant advance in; that the man-apes who had the genetic potentialities for this form of behavior possessed genetic potentials for intelligence which distinguished them from all other creatures. That is the real significance of the evidence of the tools. Man is man not merely because he is a toolmaker, but also because he is the creature and the creator of intelligence. Man, indeed, is man because there has been a continuous feedback, a reciprocal evolutionary interaction, between his toolmaking activities and his intelligence.

Virtually all animals possess some degree of intelligence.[11] Man differs from other animals principally in the degree to which his intelligence has developed beyond theirs. Intelligence, as we have already said, is a form of problem-solving behavior; but so is instinct, and although instinct has been described as lapsed intelligence, it is not at all the intelligence of which we are speaking here. Intelligence is distinguished from instinctive behavior by (1) the ability to deal effectively with problems or tasks involving abstractions, (2) the ability to learn, and (3) the ability to deal with new situations. Instinct, on the other hand, is an innate, unlearned tendency to react in a particular manner to a particular stimulus, accompanied by a particular emotion. Instinct is an enduring tendency to act in an organized and biologically adaptive way that is characteristic of a given species. Intelligence is free of the biological predeterminants which condition the behavior of the animal that is reacting instinctively. When an animal behaves instinctively, it is *reacting* to a stimulus. When an animal behaves with intelligence, it is *responding*. Instinct is without thought. Intelligence always involves thinking, a choice between alternatives, and the inhibition of inappropriate responses or response tendencies. Instinct reacts virtually automatically. Intelligence inhibits (and, indeed, that is what the cortex, the gray matter of the brain, has become, an organ, among other things, of inhibition); it considers alternatives, says "Let me think this over," and having arrived at a considered judgment, acts.

An intelligent act, then, involves (1) understanding the relations that exist between the elements of a problem and (2) the invention of the appropriate solution. Most animals are capable of varying degrees of such behavior, but man excels them all in this capacity. It is for that reason that all men, *Homo*, should be designated *sapiens*, from the very first men onward, for their characteristic trait, separating them from all other creatures, is the capacity for intelligent behavior. But the term has traditionally been reserved for later forms of man. It should, however, always be remembered that from the outset intelligence has been the outstanding characteristic of man in all his varieties, however early, however primitive, and however separated from the main streams of human events. It is this characteristic, the most important of all his tools, his intelligence, that has brought man so far, and, we may dare hope, will take him yet further along the road of his evolutionary destiny. Indeed, the study of man's evolution is the study of the evolution of successful responses to environmental pressures, as opposed to instinctive reactions.

Physical tools confer immense survival benefits upon their makers and are the product of the most powerful of all man's tools, his intelligence. Intelligence is, indeed, the most powerful form of adaptive behavior in the total equipment of man. The elements of intelligence, its concepts, rational principles, methods, and the like, constitute a set of mental implements, which man has to invent and perfect, and which he must learn to handle.[12] These concepts or mental implements represent the condensations of experience, which, in the form of abstract symbols, constitute summaries of our knowledge of particular classes of experience. Those classes of experience may be organic, inorganic, living, nonliving, material, or mental. We shall repeatedly return to the discussion of the evolution of intelligence in the appropriate places, for the growth of intelligence is the main stream which develops into the refreshing river that carries our story of the rise and early development of man along with it.

Who, then, were the man-apes in whom this intelligence, which the great French philosopher Henri Bergson defined as "the capacity to construct artificial objects; in particular, tools,"[13] first appeared? Note that intelligence is identified by Bergson with the capacity—meaning ability—to make tools.

The Earliest Known Men

In South Africa, since 1925, there have been discovered a number of fossil man-apes who are called the "Apes of the South," the australopithecines. The skeletal remains of the australopithecines exhibited a fascinating mixture of ape- and manlike traits. For example, the total appearance of the

FIG. 6 Skull of juvenile *Australopithecus africanus*. (*Courtesy of Prof. Raymond Dart.*)

skull was that of an ape, but in such details as the form, shape, and size of the teeth, the absence of a simian gap (except in the case of the young *Australopithecus· africanus* found at Taung) owing to the reduced size of the canine teeth, the position of the foramen magnum at the base of the skull which showed that the head was carried erectly upon the neck, all testified to these creatures being well along the road to man-like, hominid, status. Subsequently, the pelvic, leg, and foot bones of these creatures were found, and these showed beyond any doubt that they were bipedal and moved habitually in an erect position. But with all these hominid features there was one which made it very difficult for many authorities to accept the possibility that these were in fact early men and not apes. This was the small size of the brain.

Brain size in fossil skulls is determined by measuring the cranial capacity, that is, the volume of the interior of the skull or brainbox. Cranial capacity provides one with a fair measure of the volume of the brain. In the australopithecines cranial capacity is never more than 650 cubic centimeters. Adult male gorillas have been recorded with as large a brain volume, and even larger, in one case as much as 752 cc. Most authorities had always believed that a brain volume below 750 cc. could not function as that of a man. The distinguished English physical anthropologist, the late Sir Arthur Keith, had called this limit of 750 cc. the "Cerebral Rubicon." Since the australopithecines had not crossed that Rubicon it was argued that they could therefore not be men, even though, as Sir Arthur wrote, "in structure of body and in form of brain [they] come much nearer to man than they do any of the living forms [of ape]."[14]

There seemed good reason, indeed, to believe that a brain of less than 750 cc. could not be human. Brains of lower volume among adult human beings were almost invariably associated with extreme mental deficiency. What was over-looked was the fact that even the most extremely deficient of such small-brained individuals were capable of a good many behavioral traits of which apes are not. Be that as it may, the case for the australopithecines viewed as advanced manlike apes rather than early forms of man seemed reasonable, except, as we shall see, to their principal protagonist, Professor Raymond Dart.

As the fossil remains both of the australopithecines and those of associated animals accumulated, two main types began to emerge. The type from which the group takes its name,

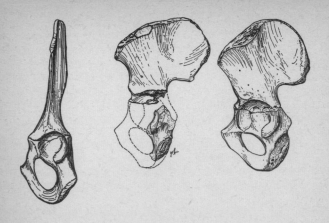

FIG. 7 The pelvis of *Australopithecus* (center) compared with that of contemporary man (Bushman) and that of a chimpanzee (left). Though there are significant differences in detail (representing significant functional differences), the resemblance of the australopithecine pelvis to that of contemporary man is striking. In each case the pelvis presents a left lateral view of a male adolescent. (*Courtesy of Prof. Raymond Dart and the* AMERICAN JOURNAL OF PHYSICAL ANTHROPOLOGY.)

Australopithecus, was recognized as a distinct genus because it possessed a distinct forehead, a moderately developed zygomatic arch (cheekbone), no sagittal crest on top of the skull, reduced canine teeth, and a cranial capacity of between 450 and 550 cc. The teeth show that the members of this group were omnivores.

Another type, very much more robustly built than *Australopithecus,* was placed in the genus *Paranthropus.* This form, found at Swartkrans in South Africa, had much reduced canines and incisors, but large premolar and molar teeth. There is no forehead to speak of, a sagittal crest is present, and the zygomatic arches are strongly developed (Fig. 9). Cranial capacity is between 450 and 550 cc. On the evidence of the teeth it has been argued that *Paranthropus* was a vegetarian, at least in this part of Africa. But this is quite conjectural and almost certainly incorrect. In some parts of Africa, including the Swartkrans region, corridors of woodlands or forests might well have provided a form like *Paranthropus* with all the food it required and placed no pressures upon it to extend its diet from plant to animal food. In other parts of

FIG. 8   Reconstruction of an australopithecine hunting scene. (*From a painting by Maurice Wilson.*)

Africa, in which forms like *Paranthropus* occurred (and the remains of nearly 200 specimens are known), they had added meat to their diet. These facts could be highly significant, for if it were establishable that in a forested region *Paranthropus* remained a vegetarian, but in an arid or semi-arid region took to augmenting his diet with meat, we would have in this a striking demonstration of the importance of the difference in ecology as a factor pressuring and evoking the necessary adaptive response. It would agree well with the view that it was the changing environment from a woodlands or forest habitat to a savanna ecology, arid, and with inadequate vegetation to sustain the life of a small wandering group, that forced

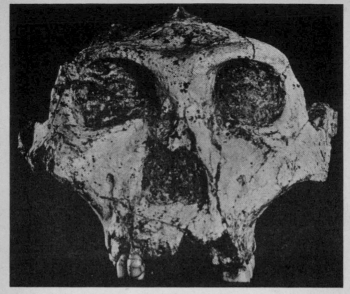

FIG. 9 Skull of *Paranthropus robustus*. (*Courtesy of the American Museum of Natural History*.)

the adoption of meat eating as a vital supplement to the plant diet that had served most primates as their virtually exclusive diet for some seventy million years.

Paranthropus, being morphologically the more primitive form, appears to have been the direct ancestor of *Australopithecus*. Both are australopithecines, the one being morphologically less advanced than the other. Culturally *Australopithecus* was also more advanced than *Paranthropus*. There is, however, a form virtually identical with, and certainly most closely related to, *Paranthropus,* namely *Zinjanthropus boisei,* discovered in East Africa in July, 1959, that has taught us more about the transition from man-ape to man than has any other discovery ever made in the evolutionary history of man. This discovery has literally revolutionized our understanding of the nature of those evolutionary factors which were responsible for the appearance of man on this earth. The story of the Human Revolution is also the story of the revolution in anthropological thinking which the understanding of that story has brought about. We may now proceed with the story of this great discovery and its significance.

The Significance of Oldoway Man

For thirty years Dr. L. S. B. Leakey[15] and his wife, Mary Leakey, had worked, whenever they could, in Olduvai Gorge in Tanganyika Territory, East Africa, in search of the remains of fossil men they were convinced must lie buried there. From the lowest deposits, at the very base of the Pleistocene, they had recovered the earliest type of stone tools ever made. From the bed in which they were found these tools are called Oldowan. Examples of these are shown in Fig. 10. Oldowan-type tools have been found in many other parts of Africa, but it was not until 17 July 1959 that they were found by Mary Leakey in association with one of their makers—the oldest well-established toolmaker thus far discovered. On the living-floor on which the skeletal remains were found were also found the skeletal remains of the food of Oldowan man, together with the tools he had made on the spot. We shall describe these tools in a moment, but first let us proceed with the account of the hominid skeletal remains and the associated fauna.

Zinjanthropus boisei ("Zinj" after the classical Arabic name for East Africa, and the specific name "boisei" after an English benefactor) is represented by an almost complete skull without mandible, the larger part of the tibia or shin-bone, and its lateral mate, the fibula.

The skull is that of a youth between the ages of 16 and 18 years. Cranial capacity was 530 cc., and stature is estimated to have been about 4 feet 9 inches. The saggital crest is well

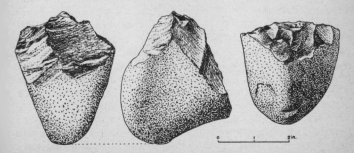

FIG. 10 Oldowan pebble-tools (lava), from Bed I, Olduvai Gorge, Tanganyika. (*Courtesy of the British Museum [Natural History].*)

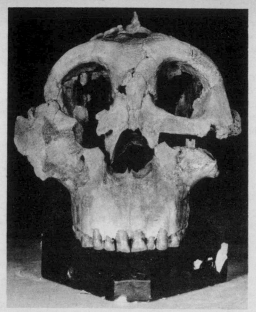

FIG. 11a   Frontal view of skull of *Zinjanthropus boisei*. (*Copyright Des Bartlett, Armand Denis Productions.*)

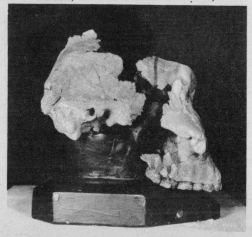

FIG. 11b   Right lateral view of skull of *Zinjanthropus boisei*. (*Copyright Des Bartlett, Armand Denis Productions.*)

developed, there is practically no brow, and the torus above
the eyesockets, the supraorbital torus, is massive. The width
between the eyes (interorbital width) is enormous, and
achieves the rare morphological distinction of exceeding the
breadth of the nasal aperture. The nasal bones are long and
narrow, and are broader superiorly than they are inferiorly,
and are only slightly elevated in a median ridge. The face is
long and wide, and the facial and cheekbone portions of the
skull are enormous, as is the depth of the body of the upper
jaw, the maxilla. The palate is exceedingly high. It is surprising to find a strongly developed anterior nasal spine in so
projecting a jaw, a markedly human characteristic indicating
the presence of a projecting cartilaginously based fleshy nose.
The canine and incisor teeth are as small as, if not smaller
than, they are in contemporary *Homo sapiens,* and there is
no premaxillary diastema in the upper jaw. The premolars
and molars, however, are enormous—almost twice the width
of modern man's! All the teeth are in the jaws and are perfectly preserved. They show evidences of wear such as is
seen among food gatherers who take in a great deal of grit
with their plant foods. The third molars, which are smaller
than the second molars—as in man—had not yet erupted beyond the gum level, and are particularly interesting because
they show a crinkling of the occlusal surface similar to that
seen in the orang-utan. It is also of great interest to note that
the right upper lateral incisor is smaller than its counterpart
on the left side of the jaw, a condition which is occasionally
seen in contemporary man, while the incisors, if anything, are
smaller than those of contemporary man. This is both surprising and most interesting in view of the large size of the
premolars and molars, for what this almost certainly tells us
is that in the evolution of the hominid dentition, the incisor-
canine series underwent reduction before the premolar-molar
series. This is confirmed by the conditions seen in later forms
of man (such as *Homo erectus* [*Pithecanthropus*] *robustus*).
Another well-developed hominid character is the presence of
a large mastoid process. The large foramen, the foramen
magnum, at the base of the skull is situated even more toward
the frontal plane than it is in the skull of modern man, a really
extraordinary finding, and one which leaves little doubt that
Zinjanthropus habitually walked erectly.

The skull was found on a living-floor beside the bank of
what was once a lake, in Bed I of Olduvai Gorge (Figs. 11
a, b), associated with Oldowan pebble tools. These tools are

characterized by the fact that only a few flakes have been removed from the stone in either one or two directions on both faces to make a simple chopping tool with a sharp but irregular cutting edge on either the side or edge of the stone (Fig. 10). These are the typical tools of Oldowan industry. The characteristic tool in Bed I at Olduvai is the pebble chopper flaked on two or more faces, but pebble choppers that have been worked on one side only occur quite frequently at Olduvai. In the presence of the unilateral flaked tools at Olduvai, together with bilaterally flaked pebble choppers, we see the probable sequence in the development from unilateral to bilateral flaking and the persistence of the two stages in the same industrial tradition.

Since at the Olduvai I level only clay occurs naturally and there is no stone whatever, the materials from which *Zinjanthropus'* tools were made, quartzite and lava, must have been brought from a distance. On the living-floor, associated with the skull, there were found 9 choppers, 1 hammerstone, 5 natural stones, and 176 flakes, indicating that the tools were manufactured on the spot.

Associated with the remains of *Zinjanthropus* were the remains of his food. This consisted of baby pigs and baby antelopes, whose bones he had split open for their marrow, and also rats, mice, frogs, lizards, snakes, tortoises, and birds. These are all small animals that can be collected with one's bare hands. There were no remains of large adult animals. As a matter of fact, *Zinjanthropus* lived during a period when many animals were passing through a phase of gigantism. He was surrounded on all sides by gigantic animals, by pigs as large as rhinos, sheep that stood seven feet high at the shoulder, giant hippos, cattle, antelopes, and baboons. These creatures he left unmolested.

Zinjanthropus was found at a depth approximately 22 feet below the upper limit of Bed I. Since the Olduvai I beds belong to the Lower Pleistocene, *Zinjanthropus* becomes the earliest known toolmaker whose remains have been found. How early? The answer to that question is one of the remarkable aspects of the whole story. Until the dating of *Zinjanthropus* was established, it had been believed that the Pleistocene could not be older than between 600,000 and a million years. Dr. Leakey estimated the age of *Zinjanthropus* at about 600,000 years or possibly more. Some authorities thought that this was too much. But when the rock, a volcanic tuff or ash, in which *Zinjanthropus* had been for so long en-

FIG. 12 Dr. L. S. B. Leakey and son, Phillip, at Olduvai Gorge. (*Copyrighted by National Geographic Society.*)

tombed was subjected by two geologists from the University of California at Berkeley to a novel method of determining the age of such rocks, the results were quite astonishing. The method used is known as the potassium-argon dating method. The potassium-argon method is based on the fact that all natural potassium contains 0.01 per cent of the parent radioactive isotope potassium-40, which decays into the daughter elements calcium-40 and argon-40 at a half-life rate of 50 per cent every 1.25 billion years (1.3×10^9 years). By determining the amount of potassium-40 that has decayed into argon-40, it is possible to determine the passage of time since the rocks were laid down. Inasmuch as the volcanic eruptions occurred both before and after *Zinjanthropus* lived, the volcanic tuff sandwich in the *Zinjanthropus* remains in such a manner that a good check can be made on his age, within a few thousand years. By means of this method, which has since been several times confirmed, Drs. Jack F. Evernden and Garniss H. Curtis, of the University of California, have determined the age of *Zinjanthropus* at about 1,750,000 years! This is about twice the age that had formerly been conceded to man as an inhabitant of this earth. And that age, surprising as it was to almost everyone, forms a consistent part of the story of the development of our understanding of the history of man. From the day in the seventeenth century when Bishop Lightfoot, Vice-Chancellor of the University of Cambridge, announced that Man was created by the Trinity at 9:00 o'clock of a Monday morning on the 23rd of October in the year 4000 B.C., the story has been the same: the duration of man's history on earth, the more we have learned about it, has progressively lengthened. No one, however, was prepared for the enormous increase that the dating of *Zinjanthropus* gave for the time that man has been man. Actually that date means that the very first men are even older than that.

Morphologically *Zinjanthropus* is not significantly distinguishable from *Paranthropus* of Swartkrans, South Africa. *Zinjanthropus*, therefore, should be regarded as the common name of the East African representative of the *Paranthropus* group of australopithecines. *Zinjanthropus* is a member of the morphologically most primitive form of man, and possibly a member of the stock or very close to the stock that made the transition from protoman to man. In any event, he provides us with virtually all the evidence we need with which to reconstruct the passage of near-man to man. He tells us not quite everything, but more than enough to enable us to follow the course of the early evolution of man, so that we can now, for the first time, reconstruct that history with a great deal more security, and much more revealingly, than most of us thought would be possible this side of the twentieth century. Much of that evolution has taken a course which was the opposite of what most authorities had believed. For example, it had always been believed that the brain increased in size before toolmaking became possible. It had been taken for granted by most authorities that the adoption of the erect posture followed the increase in the size of the brain, that walking preceded the ability to run, and so on. The exact opposite is, as we shall see, the truth. When, therefore, on an earlier page I said that the Human Revolution, when it at long last came to be understood, constituted also a revolution in anthropological thinking, those words were solidly based on the shock of recognition that the facts, as they were finally revealed, made a good deal more sense than the conjectures of the most respected authorities. It is always well to remember that an authority is one who *should* know.

The significances, rather than the significance, of *Zinjanthropus* are so many that they rush upon one almost with an embarrassment of riches. Let us attempt to deal with them in some sort of systematic order. The following, then, are the facts with which the *Zinjanthropus* finds provide us concerning the early history of human evolution.

The erect posture (bipedalism) was achieved long before the attainment of a large brain. In fact, the evidence indicates that the advance from the obliquely quadrupedal method of locomotion to erect bipedalism was achieved before the invention of toolmaking. Indeed, the erect posture constitutes a necessary condition before toolmaking is likely to be initiated, because it frees the upper extremities and hands for functions which the quadruped is unlikely to pursue, particularly when chasing small animals that are attempting to escape. To some extent most monkeys and apes can run bipedally, especially when carrying things, though they habitually progress on all fours when on the ground. Walking is not as easy for them as running. With the adoption of the erect posture, walking became as easy as running and enjoyed a high selective value because it enabled the individual to move slowly and quietly in seeking out and capturing the small and juvenile animals and the slow-moving ones. The erect posture facilitated the scanning of distance and extending to moving objects in the distance the stones which one could throw beyond the limits afforded by one's upper extremities. In short, the limitations of anatomical structure could be extended by utilizing the upper extremities to energize the otherwise inert stones and other objects which could then be forcefully thrown at the quarry. The beginnings of hunting of this kind would arise naturally under the small-game-gathering activities of early man, when in his attempt to "collect" a young animal, it would take off and he would then have to give chase and attempt to bring it down. Since there was no stone at Olduvai, it may be that something resembling a spear was thrown. But for this we have no evidence, and if wooden spears were used they would have crumbled to dust long ago. It may be that *Zinjanthropus* had other methods of collecting game. Whatever these were, free hands would have been a great help. We know that *Zinjanthropus* was also a fisherman from the find, at a second site, lower and earlier than the first, at Olduvai, of the bones of catfish and tortoises. These animals are inhabitants of shallow water and are slow-moving, easily caught creatures. So that even in seeking out fish *Zinjanthropus* was still a food gatherer. This is the first evidence we have of any primate ever having extended his food gathering from the land into water. Since the teeth of *Zinjanthropus* and *Paranthropus* are so much alike, doubt is thrown upon the claim that *Paranthropus* was a vegetarian.

The erect posture raises man up toward the heavens and greatly enlarges the space of recognition that he may now embrace. Perhaps something of this is encapsulated in the very word for "man" which the Greeks used, namely, *anthropos,* which is said to have its roots in a word originally meaning "He who looks upward." Among mammals man is the only creature that is erect and, indeed, in the whole animal kingdom, one of the few creatures that habitually look upward and forward, and thus extends both the range and dimension of his vision. The erect posture places a high premium upon the sense of vision, and this undergoes progressive development. It is often stated that the sense of smell has declined in importance in man, and that this is in part connected with the shrinkage in the projection of the face and jaws. This, however, is almost certainly not true. The sense of smell has always been of the greatest adaptive value to man, and his well-developed nose makes available a large mucous area which is richly endowed with olfactory receptors. The erect posture, the development of a dominantly visual brain, and the development of the hands, together with the extension of their functions in the form of toolmaking, hereafter evolve interactively and closely together.

The brain size of *Zinjanthropus* is that of an ape, and the skull looks in most respects like that of an ape. But *Zinjanthropus* is a man, *not* an ape. The cranial capacity, which roughly corresponds to brain size, has been determined at 530 cc. in *Zinjanthropus.* In the fully grown adult, cranial capacity may have reached 700 cc. This is still below the "Cerebral Rubicon" of 750 cc. *Zinjanthropus* forever disposes of the "Cerebral Rubicon" and tells us that it is not so much the size of the brain as its genetic quality that is the important thing. It is not weight, nor size, nor external form, nor structure that counts, nor the number of convolutions of the brain, but the genetic potentialities for symbolic thought. Many a reputation has been lost in the sinuous convolutions of the brain in the attempt to prove that one or another of its visible structures is responsible for the difference in achievement between individuals and populations. The appearance presented by the brain has nothing whatever to do with its functional qualities, qualities which are dependent in the last analysis upon the molecular structure of the genes subserving those functions. At some time in an australopithecine group or population immediately ancestral to the australopithecines, a simple gene mutation had occurred which preadapted those individuals to whom the mutation was transmitted to respond to novel environmental challenges rather more successfully than those not possessing such a genotype (genetic constitution). A mutation is a change in the basic property of a gene resulting in a transmissible hereditary modification in the expression of a trait. Gene mutations provide the raw materials of evolution, and those mutations which, under the particular conditions prevailing at a particular time level, confer some advantage upon their possessors in the effort to survive are likely to establish themselves within a population, and enable the members of that population to leave a larger progeny behind them than those individuals who do not happen to possess the favorable mutant genes. This is the principle of *differential fertility* at work, or, as it is more often called, *natural selection*. In the "struggle" for existence those individuals are likely to survive and leave a larger progeny who possess the necessary adaptive fitness which enables them, by and large, to "struggle" effectively with whatever challenges are presented to them. By "population" is to be understood any contiguously distributed grouping of a single species which is characterized by both genetic and cultural continuity through several generations. Throughout the greater part of man's history populations were nearer the order of a few score than a few hundred.

It should not have been expected that a sudden leap would have occurred from a brain of ape size to one of considerably larger size before it could become capable of functioning in a human manner. In nature sudden leaps of that kind are rare. Evolution works largely by the accumulation of small mutant changes, and this is what occurred in the evolution of man. The change that took place in the first potentially human creatures was genetic, for without that genetic change they could not have taken the step—not leap—from apedom to humanity. Toward that end, increase in brain quantity was unnecessary, but increase in brain quality was essential. Increase in brain quantity followed only upon the increase in the demands that a new way of life, culture, imposed upon early man. It was not that the brain increased in size first in order to enable early man to meet the challenges of the environment, but rather the other way round. The challenges, the pressures, of the environment favored brains which possessed the fortuitously favorable arrangements which enabled their possessors to adapt successfully to the environment. This feedback between cultural adaptation and environmental pressure gradually led to an increase in brain size in order to house those multiplying structural arrangements upon which the new way of life placed so high an adaptive premium, or as the technical term has it, *selection pressure*. By selection pressure is meant the measure of the action of selection in tending to alter the frequency of a gene and its expression in a population.

Thus, the *Zinjanthropus* discoveries topple two formerly well-entrenched beliefs: the one, that the brain must be of a large size before it can function in a human manner, and the other, that the morphological appearance (that is, the structure and form) of the skull must be dominantly manlike rather than what we believe to be apelike before its possessor can be said to be human. Both beliefs are now shown to be unsound, and both underscore the fact that too much emphasis, in the past, has been placed upon morphological traits, and insufficient attention has been paid to functional ones. Indeed, the definition of man, which defines what is essentially human about him, is not a matter of physical structure but a matter of functional capacity, the capacity for complex symbol usage, a definition which embraces the capacity to make tools. It should always be remembered that as a toolmaking animal, man's most important tools are his concepts, his symbols.

Toolmakers before Zinjanthropus at Olduvai

The zinjanthropines were not the earliest men. Toolmakers were already flourishing more than half a million years before *Zinjanthropus boisei*. This became clear when in 1962, at the lowermost site thus far explored at Olduvai by Leakey, a living-floor was found which, by means of the potassium-argon method, has been dated back to 1,860,000 years. This is by far the oldest date for toolmaking thus far obtained, and pushes the antiquity of man much further back than even the most radical students of man thought possible.

The living-site contained several hundred beautifully made small tools, together with the shattered bones of animals, evidently cracked open in order to obtain the marrow. The smallness of the tools suggests a creature with small hands and short stature (see p. 68).

FIG. 13 *Zinjanthropus* palate and teeth compared with those of modern man (below.) (*Copyright Des Bartlett, Armand Denis Productions.*)

Becoming an Omnivore

The transition from a vegetarian diet to an omnivorous diet is beautifully and, as it were, occlusally exhibited, by both the morphology of the teeth and jaws and by the skeletal remains of *Zinjanthropus'* food. Reference has been made to the smallness of the incisor-canine series of teeth and to the enormous size of the premolar teeth in *Zinjanthropus* (Fig. 13). In these size differences we have good evidence of, as it were, the evolution of the hominid dentition in process. We observe it proceeding, almost before our eyes, for the large premolar-molar teeth are associated with a vegetarian diet, in which the crushing and grinding of plant foods are facilitated by such teeth with large occlusal surfaces, and the small canine-incisor series are associated with the use of tools and with meat eating. It has already been noted that meat requires much less chewing than fibrous plants. Large canine teeth are indispensable for shredding the harder coverings of many edible plants (e.g., saplings), and bony crests, such as the sagittal crest in a number of australopithecines, including *Zinjanthropus*, are necessary to give attachment to the massive temporal muscles that are largely responsible for the major movements of the lower jaw of the plant-eating ape. With the advent of toolmaking and an omnivorous diet, large shredding and cutting teeth, like the canines and incisors, were no longer necessary, for tools could do very much more efficiently what canine and incisor teeth can do only much less efficiently. In short, when tools began to take over the functions of the incisor-canine series, these teeth proceeded to undergo reduction in size. With the reduction in size of the canines especially, there was no longer any necessity for the simian gap (premaxillary diastema) for the accommodation of the tips of

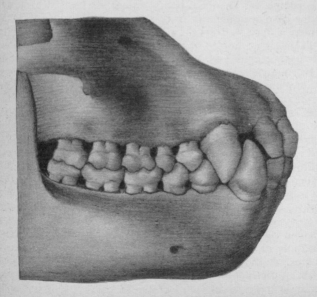

FIG. 14 The "Simian gap," or premaxillary diastema, in an adult female chimpanzee.

the lower canines, and so the simian gap became obliterated after the reduction in the size of the canines. We know this to have been the order of events from the fact that in *Homo* (*Pithecanthropus*) *erectus robustus,* an early man from the Lower Pleistocene of Java, a simian gap of some 5 millimeters is present, together with a much reduced canine on both sides of the jaw (Fig. 14).

The effect of such a reduction in the incisor-canine series and the obliteration of the simian gap would be to reduce the forward projection of the jaws considerably, and to cause the roots of the teeth to assume vertical positions in the jaws rather than the sloping positions characteristic of apes. With the progressive increase in these developments, the jaws would withdraw to a position in the plane directly below the eyes. With this verticalization of the face (orthognathy), the nasal bones would become elevated and rotated outward and forward to produce the bony projection of the nose with its lower cartilaginous half projecting from the face, the only primate (not excluding the proboscis monkey) in which this occurs. In *Zinjanthropus* these changes are already initiated, but far from completed. The nasal bones are not markedly projecting, but the developed anterior nasal spine at the base of the nasal opening is very well developed, facts which indicate that the cartilaginous portion of the nose was rather more developed than its upper part (Fig. 15). Thus, we begin to see what an enormous effect the addition of meat to the diet had upon the development of man's head. With the reduction in the size of the teeth there was no longer any reason for sagittal crests, and so these would gradually become reduced, until with the great expansion of the cranium the temporal muscles would find attachment to the upper parts of the sides of the skull rather than to the top. In *Zinjanthropus* the sagittal crest is still well developed, as it would have to be in the presence of such enormous premolar and molar teeth, and the upper jaw (and we may be quite certain the lower jaw) was quite massive. The upper jaw is, of course, nonmovable. It is the lower jaw which it is the sole function of the temporal muscles to aid in raising and retracting (i.e., in closing). It is by the relaxation of this and the action of the lateral pterygoid muscles that the mandible is lowered, the mouth opened. That all the muscles of mastication—the paired masseters, temporals, lateral and medial pterygoids—were strongly developed in *Zinjanthropus* is also very evident from the enormous development of the zygomatic processes (cheekbones) to

FIG. 15   Reconstruction of appearance of *Zinjanthropus*. (*From a painting by Peter Bianchi; courtesy of the National Geographic Society.*)

which the masseters are attached, and which in turn are attached to the greater part of the ramus of the mandible, and
from the great development of what remains of the pterygoid
plates, as well as from the great volume of the temporal fossae
which are filled by the temporal muscles. With the reduction
in the premolar and molar teeth, the mandible would have
undergone reduction in size accompanied by a correlated reduction in the size of the muscles attached to it. This, in turn,
would have led to a reduction in the depth of the upper jaw,
in the direction of the form subsequently exhibited by later
men.

It has already been remarked that the canine-incisor teeth
in *Zinjanthropus* are, if anything, smaller than they are in
contemporary man. This interesting fact suggests the remarkably sensitive manner in which morphological changes reflect
the changes in food habits, for with a diet in which the meat
part was largely restricted to the tender muscles of young
animals, the canine-incisor teeth would, indeed, not need to
be as large as they would tend to be in the eaters of large

game. The "worrying" of the meat that the eaters of large game indulge in puts a considerable strain upon the front teeth. Such strain was absent in the case of the zinjanthropines, because the meat they ate was restricted to that of young animals, hence the small size of their front teeth. Here, then, we have a striking example of the relation of the way of life of an organism to its morphological structure in process of evolution, as it were, before our very eyes. At the same time it also constitutes an illuminating example of the manner in which the right kinds of fossil finds enable us to reconstruct the interaction of the various organic and ecological factors which were at work during the early evolution of man.

Changes in the form of the teeth do not occur overnight, and from the evidence of the teeth of *Zinjanthropus* the indications are that his plant- and animal-gathering way of life lasted for many thousands of years. How long it is now possible to say with some degree of accuracy as a consequence of Leakey's discovery in January, 1964, of an almost complete adult zinjanthropine jaw with all the teeth in place. This was found in a deposit with fauna of Middle Pleistocene age, at a new site west of Lake Natron, northeast of Olduvai. The deposit is almost 500,000 years later than that from which the original zinjanthropine skull was recovered, and indicates that for this long period of time the zinjanthropines scarcely underwent any morphological change.

Some 250 yards from the site of the discovery of *Zinjanthropus*, at another site and at a lower level than the original discovery, the Leakeys found, in the summer of 1960, a large part of the left footbones, six fingerbones, two ribs, two collarbones, the parietal or dome bones of the skull, and the lower jaw with thirteen teeth still in place, all belonging to a child of about 12 years of age. In association were a large number of typical Oldowan artifacts, including a most interestingly shaped bone tool, which Leakey interprets as some sort of "lissoir," a tool used for working and polishing the skins of animals into usable leather. If the interpretation of the significance of this bone tool is correct, and it would seem to be, then as Leakey remarks, "It postulates a more evolved way of life for the makers of Oldowan culture than most of us would have expected." Great quantities of the remains of tortoises, catfish, and relatively easily caught aquatic birds were found at this level, indicating that at this stage these early men had not yet progressed to the gathering and killing of the juveniles of larger animals.

FIG. 16 Development of the three stages of hunting. (*Drawings by Donald S. Miller.*)

We have, then, in these finds a step-by-step account of the manner in which the omnivorous diet evolved in man: first, by the extension of the habit of food gathering to the slow-moving, easily caught animals, including tortoises, catfish, and aquatic birds, followed by the extension of this to the collection of the young of larger animals, and finally to the hunting of the larger animals themselves—but the latter is a part of the story to which we have yet to come. It is a natural progression, but only a few years ago we had not even the vaguest idea as to the nature of the progression. Today the story is quite otherwise as a result of the findings made at Olduvai since 1959.

Man as a Toolmaker

Was the second find at Olduvai that of an australopithecine? Most authorities would have been willing to hazard the guess that it almost certainly should have been. Their astonishment may well be imagined when on 4 April 1964 Dr. Leakey and his colleagues P. V. Tobias and John R. Napier announced that the second series of finds at Olduvai were those of a completely new form of man, whom they named, because of his skill as a toolmaker, *Homo habilis*.

At the same level of Bed I where the remains of the 12-year-old child were found were also the remains of an adult comprising a collarbone, several fingerbones, and the fragment of a heavily worn premolar or molar tooth. The site has been dated at about 1,860,000 years by the potassium-argon method. It is, therefore, about 100,000 years earlier than the original *Zinjanthropus* site. In addition to the bone "lissoir" there were found choppers, together with horn and waste flakes, and the metatarsal and metacarpal bones of antelopes sharpened to a point. These latter tools were striated in a manner indicating that they had been used for digging roots. The associated animal bones have already been mentioned above.

The cranial capacity of the Bed I child was about 680 cc., possibly 723 cc. This means that the adult cranial capacity may have been somewhat more than 800 cc.

The recovered footbones show most of the specializations associated with the erect posture, though the form of the

FIG. 17 The power grip of which many monkeys, all apes, and men are capable. Used by man where a secure and strong grip is required for performing an act in which the elements of delicacy and precision are of secondary importance. The object is held as in a clamp between the flexed fingers and the palm, reinforcement and counter-pressure being supported by the adducted thumb. Here the hand holds an Oldowan pebble-tool. (*Courtesy of Dr. John Napier.*)

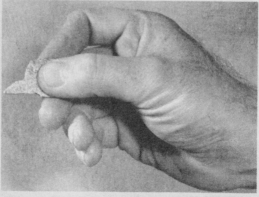

FIG. 18 The precision grip of which man alone is capable. Used by man where delicate touch and precise control of movement are required and achieved by means of a grip between the palmar aspect of the terminal phalanx of the fully opposed thumb and the terminal phalanges of the fingers. In the coarse precision grip the thumb and the tips of all the digits are involved. (*Courtesy of Dr. John Napier.*)

anklebone, the talus, upon which the shinbone (tibia) rests, is such as to suggest that the posture was not quite as fully erect as in modern man. Otherwise the form of the footbones is remarkably like that in modern man.

The handbones closely resemble those of modern man, but less so than the footbones. They are those of a terrestrial nonbrachiating form, and they differ from modern man's handbones in being more robust, the shafts of the fingerbones (phalanges) being dorsally more curved, and in several other features; but in such important points as the presence of broad, stout terminal phalanges, and the ellipsoidal form of the metacarpophalangeal joint (the palmfinger joint) indicating that, while human, the hand had not advanced quite as much toward complete hominidity as the foot. A finding entirely consistent with the fact that bipedalism was the first specifically human character to evolve, and that the development of the essentially human hand occurred later in reciprocal interaction with the developing brain. Analysis of the handbones by Napier indicates that the hands of these Olduvai forms were capable of both a strong power grip and almost certainly a precision grip (see Figs. 17 and 18).

Altogether the remains of seven individuals of *Homo habilis* have been discovered in the Olduvai region (Fig. 19), and all these remains are said to be more manlike than those of any australopithecine. Leakey, Tobias, and Napier now doubt whether *Zinjanthropus* was the maker of the tools attributed to him earlier, and believe these in fact to have been the work of *Homo habilis*. It is, however, too early to comment adequately upon these views. Whether *Homo habilis* is, indeed, a distinct species of the genus *Homo*, or an australopithecine or a pithecanthropine, it will be possible to decide (if at all) only when the necessary further studies have been completed. Until such investigations have been carried out by independent workers, the above account must be regarded as an interim report of the facts and their interpretation as of today.

Whatever the final findings it is clear that Oldoway man was already leading a rather more complexly developed cultural life than authorities had earlier thought possible. The presence of a single tool like the "lissoir" is sufficient to tell us this, because it means that these early Oldowans were already using the skins of animals, and specially preparing them with that instrument, in order to smooth out the roughnesses of the skin removed from animal carcasses. Such special preparation of animal skins could mean only one thing,

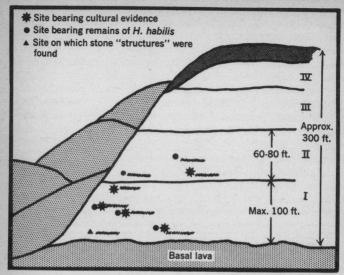

- ✳ Site bearing cultural evidence
- ● Site bearing remains of *H. habilis*
- ▲ Site on which stone "structures" were found

IV

III

Approx. 300 ft.

60-80 ft.   II

I

Max. 100 ft.

Basal lava

FIG. 19 Diagrammatic sections of beds at Olduvai Gorge showing relative stratigraphic positions of sites referred to in the text.

namely, that they were used for domestic purposes, either as mats to sleep on or as clothes, or both, and possibly even as covers for windbreaks.

If the zinjanthropines or habilines did not hunt big game, how did they secure the skins of such animals? The answer is that they probably obtained them from the carcasses of animals that had either died a natural death or been killed by some other animal. It has been suggested that these early men might also have secured some of their animal food by scavenging. Vultures, then as now, would have been the means of indicating to these early men where a carnivore had probably made a kill or an animal that had died in some other manner was to be found. This was one way of obtaining meat that has been practiced by many African peoples, among them the strandlooping Hottentots, down to the present day. The fact that the bones of large animals have not been found upon the living-floors of the early Oldowans suggests that if they did upon occasion scavenge, they ate the meat of the dead animal on the spot where it was found as, again, is frequently done by many African peoples to this day, especially when the animal is a large one like an elephant or a rhino. And if

they did carry any of the meat back with them to their home
territory it would be encumbered with as little bone as possible, and probably cut into smallish pieces. Hence, the absence of the bones of large animals on the Oldowan living-
floors. It is, of course, entirely possible that the Oldowans
were not scavengers at all. On this point we have no clearcut
evidence one way or the other. The presence of a "lissoir,"
however, makes it highly probable that large animals were
skinned, and if there was enough of the animal left to provide
a sizable skin, then it becomes highly probable that its meat
was not spurned, even if it were already "high." To this day
most nonliterate peoples are not finicky about the state of the
meat they eat. If it is edible, they eat it. In fact, many nonliterate peoples prefer their meat somewhat "high," a 'taste
which, indeed, still persists in the sophisticated hunting circles
of the Western world where the game is not considered fit to
eat until it has been hung and is a bit "high" or "gamey."

If animal skins were used as mats upon which to sleep,
were they used in the open or in caves? To this question we
do not know the answer, but since the remains of a number
of South African australopithecines, notably *Australopithecus*
(*Plesianthropus*) *transvaalensis* at Sterkfontein, *Paranthropus*
at Swartkrans, as well as *Telanthropus* (now thought to belong with *H. habilis*) from the latter site, and *Australopithecus
prometheus* from Makapansgat, were found in caves, it is
quite possible that the Oldowans made temporary use of such
natural refuges. However, it must be made clear that at the
present time there is no certain evidence that they did.

In the case of the australopithecines whose remains have
been found in caves, the evidence suggests that if these caves
were used as temporary abodes, they were not occupied for
long periods of time. Caves which are used as permanent
homes usually show a good deal of debris on their floors, the
debris of food remains and the flakes from the tools which
have been manufactured there, as well as the tools themselves.
At Sterkfontein and at Swartkrans a small number of stone
implements were found, with a much greater accumulation of
broken animal bones. This suggests several possibilities. Caves
may originally have been used as watering holes, for in the
flat, or undulating, dry dolomitic plains water is rarely found
on the surface. The best place to look for it would be in the
back parts of a cave, where the yield would be quite sufficient
to meet the needs of small bands without ever becoming
exhausted. It was almost certainly water rather than shelter

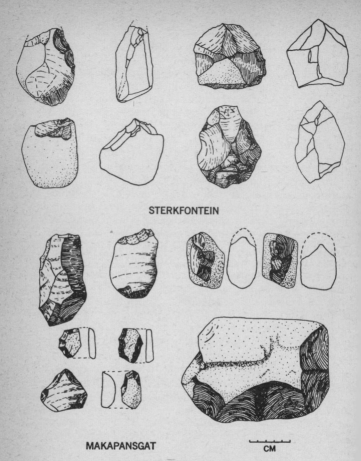

STERKFONTEIN

MAKAPANSGAT

CM

FIG. 20 Pebble stone tools from the red australopithecine breccias of
Sterkfontein and Makapansgat. (*After C. van Riet Lowe and R. J.
Mason; courtesy of Prof. Raymond Dart and Harper & Row.*)

that attracted the earliest men to caves, and once in them the
other advantages they provided would have been gradually
discovered. In order to avoid attracting other animals to a
carcass, a cave is a good place in which to butcher it. Such
activities may account for the large accumulation of animal
bones in some of the South African caves. Also, a cave makes
a good hiding place in which to lie in wait for other animals

visiting the waterholes, where they might then easily be attacked, killed, butchered, and eaten on the spot. Whenever possible, it is also a good place in which to take refuge, especially at night, as a protection against predatory animals. However, since the zinjanthropines were food gatherers, and in this term is included the gathering of small animals, they would of necessity have been compelled to wander over a considerable territory in search of food, so that a permanent habitation would not have been a possibility for them, any more than it is for most food-gathering peoples, like the Bushmen, the Australian aborigines, and the Eskimo of today. Mats made from the skins of animals were, then, probably used to sleep on wherever one bedded down for the night. But such prepared skins could have had a variety of uses; for example, they could have been used as covers to afford protection against wind, sand, rain, and sun. They could have been used as the covers for simple windbreaks, such as the Australian aborigines erected; they could also have been used as bags in which to carry a few simple belongings; and they could, as we have already said, have been used as clothes.

Habitations

In 1962 Dr. Leakey discovered several wide circles of stone in the lowermost level of Olduvai Gorge, well below the zinjanthropine and prezinjanthropine child sites. These circles were made of sizable stones, with some resting on top of the others. No such stones existed more than 2 million years ago, when the site was a lakeshore. How, then, did they get there? Who arranged them in circles? For what purpose? Leakey thinks they may be the remains of primitive dwellings or windbreaks. This is quite possible.

On the open savannas protection from the elements could have been sought by the building of simple dwellings or windbreaks. The skins of animals, as well as plant materials suitable for the purpose, could have been used to provide such shelters. The Olduvai stone circles may have served to anchor the sides of such dwellings. If such dwellings were ever used by the australopithecines or their precursors, they were almost certainly of a temporary kind, for populations that live by food gathering and hunting are unable to stay long in a single locality, but must move on from place to place in the never-ending search for food. Hence, any form of permanent dwelling would be quite unnecessary. Furthermore, since populations living at this economic level have no food materials to store in sufficient abundance to require storage space, it is unlikely that they built any structure to contain such materials.

It has sometimes been suggested that man's relatively hairless body may be a consequence of his habit of wearing clothes. The suggestion does not come from the relatively hairless Bushmen or Pygmies or the numerous other non-literate peoples of the earth who have never worn clothes. The suggestion, of course, comes from men of the Western world who habitually cover their entire bodies, with the exception of the face, with clothes. The probabilities are that for the greater part of his early history man remained unclothed; at least this would seem likely from the fact of his origin and evolution in tropical Africa. At most he may have worn a "G-string" or apron, or some headgear, or possibly a cape. Hence, it is very unlikely that clothes had anything whatever to do with man's relatively hairless condition. The elephant, the rhino, and the hippo, among other mammals, are even less well endowed with hair than man. Man's hairlessness, however, is probably not due to the same causes that brought about hairlessness in those large mammals. We shall discuss the probable cause of that hairlessness when we come to deal with those factors which served to produce some of man's other peculiarly human traits (pp. 145–148).

The consequences of the adoption of an omnivorous diet by the australopithecines were of the most far-reaching kind. In addition to changes produced in the form of the face and teeth, and the associated musculature, physiological and social changes also followed. The food provided by animal proteins is high in calories. This provides ready energy on smaller quantities than plant foods provide. Hence, where under exclusively plant-eating conditions one would tend to eat exclusively for oneself, as the apes do, meat eating would encourage the sharing of food. Thus, animals killed at a distance would not be consumed on the spot by the hunters away from their group, but would be carried back to be shared with the remaining members. This is particularly important for nursing mothers, and it is quite probable that food sharing of this kind made possible the long dependency period of the human infant upon a mother who was largely being provided for by the hunters. With individual hunters providing for their own families, in addition to providing for the other members of the group, conjugal love and group solidarity would have had a better chance to grow, and with them paternal and fraternal love, within the family and between families, making the group a communal one both as to food sharing and protection. Thus, the adoption of an omnivorous diet would have led to an extension and development of the tendencies to mutual aid and cooperation. The cooperative individual, the one who shares with his fellows, is the man most esteemed in all societies to this day, for the very simple reason that to share with others, to cooperate with others, is essential to the existence of the individual and of the group. As Sahlins has pointed out, food sharing is an outstanding functional criterion of man, a *sine qua non* of the human condition.[16]

Another of the important consequences of the new domestic-economic way of life was the emergence of the search for food as primary and the subordination of the search for mates to that drive. Toward this end socially organized arrangements would be likely to be instituted in order to secure the control of sexual expression. One such institution is kinship, the conscious recognition of the familial and other relationships between individuals, and the prescribed behavior one is expected to exhibit toward them. The satisfaction of the hunger of others becomes a primary motivation of human society, and sex a satisfaction secondary to this and to be satisfied only within the prescribed limits. Thus the individual comes to be valued for his qualities of cooperativeness, of generosity, for his service to the group. Dominance is now achieved not through bodily power, but through the power of cooperativeness, of reciprocity, of mutual aid.

The discovery of the "lissoir" at Olduvai tells us that both in intelligence and in material culture the earliest men had already made a considerable advance upon their protohuman ancestors, advances so significant that they were now, even at the earliest stages of their development, fullfledged human beings. Even so they still had a long way to go before they became fully developed ones.

The bones and stones and tools made out of hard materials are all that we have left of the zinjanthropines, but of their nonmaterial culture nothing remains except the mute testimony of such a tool as the "lissoir," which tells us that a comparatively complex culture was already under way, and had probably been under way for a long time. In 1958, in the red-brown breccia at Sterkfontein, a bone implement, 9¾ m long by 3 cm wide, was found. The bone had been split longitudinally, and one-half was then broken in a manner which produced a pointed end. The broken surfaces leading to the pointed end had been polished, by use, completely smooth. Almost certainly of australopithecine manufacture, this instrument, too, could have been used as a "lissoir," though it was probably mostly used for other purposes. Olduvai and Sterkfontein are separated by many hundreds of miles. Is it possible that there is some connection between the makers of the tools at Olduvai and those at Sterkfontein? The answer to that question is that it is more than possible, for tools of Oldowan type occur over the length and breadth of South Africa. What this means is that over the course of several thousand years the knowledge of toolmaking was carried with them by the earliest men during their wanderings and migrations over Africa south of the Sahara. This would suggest that the australopithecine phase of human development lasted scores of thousands of years, during which small populations of australopithecines were separated from their home bands, became isolated from one another, and pursued their evolutionary development apart from one another. This would account for both the physical and temporal differences which distinguish some australopithecines from others. It is possible that pebble tools were invented independently by different populations in Africa. Whether this was so or not must, however, remain an open question until further evidence becomes available.

It has seemed reasonable to some to suppose that before man used stone as a material for tools he may have used wood first, then possibly bone, and subsequently stone. Since wood is a perishable material, there are no remains that we can study. However, the earliest stone-tool maker of whom we have knowledge, the prezinjanthropine from the lower-most bed at Olduvai, was a bone- as well as stone-tool maker. This does not tell us whether bone-tool making preceded stone-tool making. Some light is thrown on this problem by the important site in South Africa, associated with *Australopithecus prometheus* at Makapansgat. At this site no stone tools were found, but numerous bones which Dart believes were deliberately manufactured by this australopithecine. These tools are made of bone, teeth, and horns, hence described by Dart as an *osteodontokeratic* culture. Both Dart and Ardrey have made out a good case for the reality of this culture, and in spite of the residue of doubt that remains among some authorities, Dart's claims have come to be treated with increasing respect. Whether all the bones were shaped by australopith-

FIG. 21 The natural osteodontokeratic (bone, tooth, and horn) tools of *Australopithecus*. Upper row: two gazelle horns and ulna (daggers and digging tools); humerus club and knife. Second row: upper jaw (scraper) and hyena lower jaw (slitting tool). Bottom: scapula, or shoulder-blade, axe. All except slitting tool from antelopes. (*Courtesy of Prof. Raymond Dart and Harper & Row.*)

cines, and whether all of them given the names by Dart served the purposes which those names suggest, will be for future research to determine, but that some of them were deliberately fashioned and used as tools is highly probable. If these bones were fashioned and used as tools by the Makapansgat australopithecines, it would appear that they probably made bone tools before they made stone ones. The flaked stones found in the Makapan cave at first were thought to have been artifacts, but have since been shown not to be so.

The bone tools made by Makapansgat australopithecines comprised, according to Dart, saws, scrapers, axes, daggers, and digging tools. The most remarkable tool described by Dart is a "scoop" made from antelope metatarsals and metacarpals (Fig. 22). At first these bones completely baffled Dart, until a visitor, on being shown a series of these scoops,

FIG. 22 Antelope cannon bones (metacarpals or metatarsals) made
into scoops (from Makapansgat) grouped about a sheep cannon-bone
apple corer from Herefordshire. (Worn-down specimens above.) (*Courtesy of Prof. Raymond Dart and Harper & Row.*)

remarked that they reminded him of the "apple corers" that
used to be made in Herefordshire for old people who had
lost their teeth but liked their apples crisp. With these implements they would work around the core of the apple, then
crush the fruit, and swallow it as a pulp. The visitor had at
his home one that his father had made in 1890 and soon
produced it for Professor Dart to photograph, and by the
kindness of Professor Dart that photograph is reproduced
here. It will be seen that the resemblance of the Makapansgat
scoops to the Herefordshire scoop is striking. The Makapansgat scoops are highly polished as with much use, and the
upper two appear to have been worn down with use.

Some of the older australopithecines may have lost their
teeth, and it is possible that such individuals were fed with
these scoops, and as Dart reasons, toothless infants may have
been weaned by having their food (not including apples—for

these were not available) scooped and pulped in this manner. The australopithecines would, then, be the first manufacturers of pulped baby foods! However ingenious they were, the Makapansgat australopithecines were not the inventors of bone tools, for the prezinjanthropines had already something of a developed bone culture, as evidenced by their "lissoir." In 1962 Dart described a "lissoir" from the Makapansgat gray breccia. Dart has also described a number of split or spirally broken flakes from the shafts of antelope long bones. The feature common to all these flakes is the presence of small grooves or indentations of varying widths. These grooves are so smooth that, according to Dart, they can only be explained on the supposition that they were used in the preparation of cords or thongs of different sizes or widths. Another antelope bone (metacarpal radius) shows a deeply scored abraded smooth transverse groove. This is highly burnished, and suggests that it was used to smooth out the roughnesses in the preparation of thongs. These findings suggest that we probably have a great deal more to learn about the already developed complex culture of the australopithecines.[17] As new discoveries continue to be made we shall learn more about the cultural life of the australopithecines at Olduvai and elsewhere. It now appears that that cultural life will turn out to be rather less simple than was formerly believed.

The osteodontokeratic industry is found among the pithecanthropines of China of the Middle Pleistocene, among the Upper Pleistocene Europeans, among the Fontéchevade people of Tayacian industry, and the European Mousterian Neanderthals who followed them. Mr. James Kitching has recently described this culture from Pinhole Cave, Creswell Crags, in Derbyshire, England, an Upper Paleolithic Mousterian site.[18] Though it is considerably later in date than the australopithecine, the resemblance between the two osteodontokeratic industries is remarkable. Whether this industry represents an unbroken tradition which has continued virtually into the present day, or whether it was several times independently invented, remains for future research to determine.

We may be fairly certain that the zinjanthropines lived in small bands, numbering not more than between half a dozen and forty or so individuals—the size of the band among nonliterate food-gathering peoples today. This is a matter to which we shall return in due course. We have now to continue with the discussion of those innovations which led to the development of humanity.

FIG. 23   Proximal end of radius of large antelope from the basal (grey) breccia at Makapansgat showing a smooth transverse groove with burnished margins above and below. These appear to have been produced by the friction of narrow strips of greenhide, which were in this manner converted into flexible thongs useful in hunting and carrying.
(Courtesy of Prof. Raymond Dart.)

The Significance of Hunting

The next behavioral development which followed, undoubtedly many millennia after the extension of plant gathering to the gathering of the juveniles of larger animals, would be the extension of such activities to the hunting of the medium-sized animals, and finally to all animals of whatever size. There is good evidence that the australopithecines had extended their food-getting activities to the hunting of medium-sized and even larger aging animals, such as baboons, antelopes, bucks, pigs, hyenas, buffalos, and rhinos. Professor Dart suggests that the Makapansgat australopithecines used as weapons antelope skulls with the horns attached. These served as axes, mattocks, and daggers. The arm- or legbones of buffalo and large buck were used as clubs or bludgeons, and when broken they could be used as stilettos. Dart also suggests that the australopithecines used crude unshaped wooden clubs.

The numerous smashed-in skulls of baboons and other animals, often found with the indentations on the skullbone where the double ridges of the lower ends of the humeri of antelopes had landed with great force, strongly confirm Professor Dart's interpretation of the hunting methods of the australopithecines. Most of the animals they hunted would be either the juveniles, the medium-sized ones, or those larger ones that had been slowed down by age. Even so, the juveniles

FIG. 24 Twelve examples of bone flakes from the basal (grey) breccia at Makapansgat showing the varying width and depth of the smooth grooves worn in the spirally broken margins, believed by Dart to have been produced by australopithecines in using them in the preparation of cords or thongs of different widths, and also in removing the bark from sticks and smoothing them for use as clubs and other hunting implements, digging sticks, and in transportation. (*Courtesy of Prof. Raymond Dart.*)

and the medium-sized animals could lead their pursuers a merry chase. The rapidly changing conditions presented by the chase would challenge the hunters to an exhibition of problem-solving behavior, designed to lead to successful results. The kaleidoscopic speed with which conditions changed during the hunt, the many problems presented, would place the highest selective value upon intelligence, and a strong negative pressure upon any kind of preconditioning of behavior such as instinct. In this way the intelligent would tend to be increasingly favored and those less well endowed with the capacity for such problem-solving behavior would not do as well in the struggle for survival—meaning by this latter phrase merely the effort to live. In this manner man very early in his career lost what remained of his instincts, and was forced increasingly to depend upon learning and intelligence, as by far the superior means for meeting the challenges of the environment. The consequences of this were enormous, and since these consequences require separate and detailed treatment, we shall postpone their discussion until we have considered some of the other consequences to which the adoption of a hunting way of life led.

It has already been pointed out that among the apes, in a forest environment, food gathering is easy; all can provide for themselves except the small infants, who are nursed by the mothers and suckled by them for several years and fed plant foods, until the young are able to forage for themselves. The adult males, and the dominant male, do not under these conditions provide food for the females and their young. With the shift into the savannas and the extension of food gathering to small slow-moving and juvenile animals, foraging would continue among the females, until with the development of hunting the economic activities of the sexes would become asymmetrically emphasized. A hominid infant is not conveniently carried on a hunting expedition; he is too large, too dependent, he may cry at an inappropriate moment and scare the game away, and he may be endangered. Furthermore, there may be other siblings who require the mother's care. Nor are pregnancy and parturition compatible with hunting. For all these reasons, and the additional ones, that she cannot run as fast as the male, and because she is muscularly less powerful than he, the female cannot be as effective a hunter. Hunting would therefore become an exclusively male occupation. In this way the first economic division of labor would come into being between the sexes. The female would remain the food gatherer, and the male would become the hunter.

The division of labor between the sexes resulting from the development of hunting, in addition to food gathering, as a way of life led to the most substantive of cultural changes. The male now becomes the provider of animal foods for the female and her young; the female provides the male with the vegetable foods. Thus cooperation and mutual aid in subsistence activities are established, and become an indispensable condition and pattern of human behavior. Food sharing is one of the most significant characteristics of man. Indeed, quite early in the evolution of man it became a vital necessity. Sharing became a way of life, and to this day the sharing of food has remained a ritual evidence of friendship and a token of involvement in the other's welfare. The willingness to share, generosity, would therefore have become a trait which would have both a high natural and social selective value, since it would substantially contribute toward the survival of the group. Mutual aid, cooperation, and generosity would take on significances far beyond the meaning they may have had at the anthropoid level.

In the hunting economy the tendency would be for one male to associate with one female, and to provide for her and her offspring. Under the strenuous conditions of early man's hunting existence the attempt to provide for more than one female and her children would in most cases have proved burdensome. There would, however, have been no strictly applied rules in this connection, and some men may very well—as in contemporary societies of the same type of economy—have protected and provided for more than one female and her offspring. Marriage, in the sense of a union between a male and female with some expectation of permanency, would thus have come into being, and monogamy, the marriage of one man to one woman, would have become established, and thus the biological family would be born, consisting of a man, his wife, and their children. This means further that while maternal-infant relationships were recognized, for the first time in the hominoid group, paternal-infant relationships are recognized—not necessarily biologically, but socially, for the paternity of a male is established by the fact that his children are the issue of his wife. In this way kinship is born. Kinship is the social recognition and expression of genealogical relationships. It is doubtful whether the relationship between sexual intercourse and the birth of children was originally connected by early man.[19] In any event kinship relationships would almost certainly have been primarily social and connected, as they are to this day in nonliterate societies, with

the generation to which an individual belonged rather than
with "blood" relationships. Thus, while recognizing one's
immediate parents as such, one would regard persons of the
same generation as one's parents as standing in the "fatherly"
and "motherly" relation to oneself, and all the children of
those fathers and mothers would be in one's brother, sister,
or cousin relationship. Persons in the grandparental generation
would be a parent's father's brother or sister, and so on. Thus
kinship would serve to regulate the behavior between the
generations.

With the birth of the biological family, or nuclear family
as it is sometimes called, obligatory relationships come into
being on the part of the parents in relation to each other and
the child, and to their society. The parents become responsible
to the group for the rearing and education of the child, and
the satisfaction of the child's needs gives rise, ultimately, to
all those cultural responses that we know.

Sex and Sociality

The apes have an estrus cycle, that is, the period during which
ovulation occurs; the sex skin in the chimpanzee, and the
labial folds in the gorilla, enlarge. During this period the
female is sexually receptive. At the end of the cycle, menstruation occurs. The period during which the anthropoid
female is sexually receptive is about 8 days in a 26-day estrus
cycle, or about a third of the duration of the estrus cycle. The
whole cycle is under hormonal control, and the male becomes
sexually interested in and associates copulatively and cooperatively with the female only when she is in heat.[20] Under
the pressure of environmental conditions associated with the
hunt, with the male becoming the active hunter, it would be
an advantage selectively if a single male attached himself
permanently to a single female. Females characterized by a
sexual receptivity that was nonperiodic, but receptive to the
male at all times, would be at a great advantage. They would
thus tend to make the interest of the male in them not a
matter of hormonal dependency but of psychologic, cortical,
control. From periodic interest this shift would be accompanied by the shift to permanent sexual interest in, and therefore permanent attachment to, the female by the male.

The feedback advantages of such a permanent bond between a single pair would be the more efficient manner in which a single male could in the hunting economy take care of the needs of a single female and their offspring, the greater domestic efficiency with which the female could minister to the needs of the family, and the greater selective advantages reciprocally conferred upon one another in the cooperative family unit thus created. Thus, monogamy is probably as old as man himself. Under such closely knit conditions conjugal love, enduring and tender, as distinguished from lust, had a better chance to grow, and with it parental and fraternal love, making the interrelated integrated family group a cooperative unit as to food, protection, and socialization. The training of the young is now assumed by both parents, and the asymmetry in the education of juvenile males and females becomes the special function of the mother for the girl, and of the father for the boy. Biological paternity may not have been recognized for a long time in the history of man, but social paternity at this time was recognized, and kinship relations were thus for the first time established. The establishment of the biological or nuclear family eventually led to the development of the extended family, embracing one's parents' paternal and maternal families. As the principal agency through which all the accumulated knowledge and wisdom of the group is transmitted, the extended family has proven of the greatest adaptive value from its very beginnings, in that it greatly increased the chances of survival of each of its members and thus of the group as a whole.

The loss of a period of heat, the estrus cycle, when the female is sexually receptive to the male, and its replacement by a diffuse sexual receptivity at all times, must have developed quite early among the progenitors of man. Where formerly sexual behavior was largely under hormonal control, it is now largely replaced by mental control. The sexual attractiveness of the female throughout the year, rather than at specific periods of heat, contributes to the attractiveness of the permanent union between male and female in human society, and constitutes another reason for the appeal of the monogamous bond. In man sexuality has been brought under cortical control. It is no longer the promiscuous sexuality of the nonhominoid primate horde, although it requires to be pointed out that the evidences of this in man still persist in many nonliterate societies in which, before marriage, promiscuous sexual relationships are freely sanctioned. In human adults the promiscuity of sex is brought under cultural control, and subordinated to ends other than sexual gratification, although the sex drive remains as powerful as ever. In the food-gathering and hunting economy the search for food transcends in importance the search for mates. Under conditions of sparsity and famine the sexual drives are the first to disappear, but the drive for food remains and, indeed, grows in intensity.

It will be understood, then, that marriage, though a social arrangement, is based on certain ineluctable ecologic conditions which render the union of male and female of advantage to them both, to their offspring, and to the group. It is not so much, as it has often been put, that marriage is regulated by the group as that the group is regulated by marriage. It is not the group that contributes to the stability of the nuclear family through marriage, but the nuclear family through marriage that contributes to the stability of the group, through its ordering of the group by means of kinship, and kinship behavior, and the development of all those cultural responses to the needs of human beings living in human societies.

The Incest Taboo

Probably one of the earliest of such cultural responses was designed to exercise some control of sexuality within the family. This is the *incest taboo,* the prohibition of sexual relations between related individuals. Many theories have been offered to explain the origin of the incest taboo. The most cogent of these, and probably the most accurate, is based on early man's almost certain observation of the fact that close inbreeding within the family sometimes led to undesirable results, in the form of abnormalities, feeblenesses of various sorts, and reproductive deficiencies. Mutations are mostly disadvantageous, and their frequency in human populations, indeed. in any population of animals, makes the ratio of deleterious and lethal recessive genes to selectively advantageous genes disproportionately high. Inbreeding within the family brings such genes together with great frequency much to the disadvantage of the family, its offspring, and the group. The prohibition of sexual relations within the family would therefore not only confer a selective advantage upon families and populations practicing the incest taboo, but would also serve to produce certain other benefits. It would solve the problem of sexual competition within the family. It would make outbreeding with members of other families the rule, and thus contribute to the cooperative binding of family to family, and of outgroup to outgroup. It would serve to train early the control of sexual expression. It would serve to provide the marriageable members of the family with mates very much more efficiently than could the family of which the individual was himself a member.

Whether the incest taboo came into being at the australopithecine level of development or later can only be conjectured at this time, but that it may have been initiated this early in the development of man remains as a possibility. The incest taboo, it may be added, is not necessarily dependent upon the recognition of physiological parentage. Explanations based on culture rather than on any understanding of the biological processes involved were, most likely, offered in order to account for the occasional ill-effects of mating between "blood" relations.

Male-Female Differentiation and Male Dominance

A fact of great importance, which very probably drew much of its force from the consequences of the sexual division of labor in a food-gathering and hunting economy, was the reinforcement of the dominance relationships of the male over the female. This would come about as a result of the increasing sexual dimorphism, that is, selection for difference in physical form, for as hunters those males would eventually be selected for survival who were not only the most intelligent but also the most physically fit. This would mean increase in body size and muscular power appreciably beyond that of the female. Increased body size would not only confer advantages in the hunt, but would also serve as a protection against predators of every kind. At the same time it would also place the male in a dominant relation to the female. This, combined with the occupational aptitudes of the male and his wide range of opportunities for learning so much more than would normally fall to the experience of the female, would greatly add to the awe in which he was held by the female, and contribute considerably to his own feeling of superiority in relation to her. But male dominance is, in fact, a socially assumed status based on socially recognized differences between the sexes, resting, it is true, upon the biological difference of greater body size and muscular power in the male, and wider experience and knowledge, the latter usually being misinterpreted as equatable with superior intelligence. Hence, from his earliest beginnings, "the world of man" has been a masculine world. In that world the female has always occupied a subordinate position. There never have been any matriarchies. The female has always taken the male's natural superiority quite as much for granted as he. Hence, from the first, obedience has been exacted both from the female and the children to rules and laws created by the male. It is the male who still makes the laws, and it is the male who still enforces them.[21]

With respect to body size the early australopithecines were about 4 feet tall and between 50 and 60 pounds in weight, while the later australopithecines were nearer the size of modern man and probably weighed no more than 100 pounds. These facts are too often overlooked when considering the brain size of the australopithecines. The australopithecine brain in relation to body size is considerably larger than the brain size of the gorilla. The gorilla weighs about four times as much as the average australopithecine weighed and has a brain size which by volume is, in fact, on the average somewhat smaller, 550 cc., than the australopithecine brain, which averaged about 600 cc. (see Table II). Thus, in relative size, the australopithecines had already achieved a rather large brain size.

The reference to brain size returns us naturally to the discussion of one of the major traits which characterize humanity, and which, indeed, played a major role in the development of humanity, namely, intelligence.

The Significance of Intelligence

We have already seen how the challenges of the savanna placed the highest premium upon problem-solving behavior, the ability to make the most successful response to the particular situation—a series of situations, indeed, which, as in hunting, frequently changed with kaleidoscopic speed. With

TABLE II

COMPARATIVE SIZE OF THE BRAIN IN MAN AND THE GREAT APES EXPRESSED AS THE PRODUCT OF THE SQUARE OF THE WEIGHT OF THE BRAIN DIVIDED BY BODY WEIGHT

Genus	Weight of brain in grams	Weight of brain to weight of body	Comparative value
Man	1,375	1:30	35.0
Chimpanzee	400	1:75	5.2
Orang-Utan	400	1:124	3.0
Gorilla	425+	1:231	2.0

Gross weight of brain without reference to total body weight is misleading. Relative brain weight, arrived at as above, yields a much more interesting comparative value, pointing to a significant increase in the relative size of the human brain.

the positive selection pressure in favor of intelligence went a negative selection pressure against instinctive behavior, a combination of selection pressures which increasingly freed early man from those preconditioners of behavior which stood in the way of successful problem-solving.

These two correlated developments, the increase in intelligence and the loss of instincts, have had the most substantive effects upon the development of humanity. These effects we may now consider in some detail. Man's genetic constitution (genotype) is such that it makes it possible for him to develop the widest possible range of behavioral adjustments and adaptations. Instead of having his responses genetically fixed as in other animal species, man is the species that invents its own responses, and it is out of this unique ability to invent, to improvise, his responses that his cultures are born. In the human species behavior may become fixed by learning, but such fixities of behavior are learned; they are not the fixed behaviors of instinct. Man, indeed, has to learn to learn. When intelligent behavior supersedes instinctive behavior and eventually completely replaces instinctive behavior as a capacity requiring development, which is what has happened in the human species, the creature so characterized must obviously learn how to function as a member of the community from other members of the group into which it is born. The consequences of this we shall discuss in a moment. For the present we would do well to turn our attention to the nature of this intelligence which is so characteristic of man, and which in undeveloped form characterized him virtually as soon as he became man.

There are many definitions of intelligence, and we have already discussed something of its nature upon an earlier page. In terms of behavior it has already been stated that intelligence constitutes (1) the ability to deal effectively with tasks involving abstractions, (2) the ability to learn, and (3) the ability to deal with new situations. These are abilities which must be learned. The capacities for these abilities are genetically based and except in identical twins are never alike in any two individuals, any more than physical traits are alike. The capacity for intelligence is at least as variable as is the variability for physical traits. Since it is through the use of intelligence that man accomplished his first successful adaptation to the challenges of the environment, and has been preserved as a species in all his remarkable variety through the continued use of that intelligence, it is desirable to understand what this remarkable trait involves. As George Stoddard has pointed out, the criteria of intelligence are recognized by the ability to undertake activities that are characterized by difficulty, complexity, abstractness, economy, adaptiveness to a goal, social value, and the emergence of originals.[22] Intelligence is not merely successfully responsive; it is also creative. In the process of solving problems it frequently creates new means of adaptation to the environment. Intelligence has evolved just as every other trait of man has. It did not suddenly spring into being in fullfledged form. The earliest form of intelligence, as Bergson first pointed out, was *practical intelligence,* the initial form of which was the ability to produce artificial objects, particularly tools. It is the intelligence which ranges from manual skill and dexterity to the inventive ability of the craftsman. Cooperation between the mind and the hand greatly contributed to the progress of man's intelligence toward the rational, logical, conceptual kind. The greatest stimulus, however, toward the development of *rational intelligence,* as it may be called, was achieved mainly through the gradual development of speech.

Speech

Speech is the expression or communication of thoughts and feelings by uttered or spoken words, vocal sounds, or gestures. When and in what manner did speech come into being? It is a question that has often been asked. Today we are in a better position to attempt an answer to that question than at any previous time. Hunting requires the cooperative endeavors of several men. Where an animal could evade a single hunter it would be less likely to do so when two or more hunters were stalking it. The selective value of cooperation in hunting would have been very high, and such hunting undoubtedly made its contribution to the development of man's cooperative nature, for a high premium would have been put upon the cooperators, and an unequivocally negative one upon the noncooperators. In every hunting society of which we have knowledge, this remains so to the present day.

Speech comes into being when two or more individuals agree to attach the same meaning to the same sounds, and thereafter use those sounds consistently with the meanings that have been bestowed upon them. The meanings are symbols which stand for things which are not present to one's senses in physical form. Speech, then, is behavior made artificially clear. It is a tool. It is the expression of intelligence, and therefore, man's most useful tool. To this day, the way a man speaks is a good indication of the quality of his intelligence.

The great apes are all capable of vocalization, varying from whines, cries, and squeaks, to screams, growls, and roars. The orang-utan and the gorilla tend to be comparatively silent and taciturn. In the natural state and in captivity the chimpanzee tends to be noisy. Anatomically the great apes *appear* to be endowed with all the vocal arrangements necessary for speech, but they do not speak. In spite of their ability to make a large range of sounds it has not been possible to teach them to speak. Possibly silence has its adaptive value under forest conditions, for life in the forest is not altogether without its hazards from predators, especially for the young ones. The apes do not speak because there were never any selective pressures upon them to adapt to their environment in such a manner.

Erect Posture and Speech

It has been suggested that the erect posture may have had something to do with those anatomical rearrangements in nose, lips, throat, and adjacent structures which, together with the necessary changes in the brain, made human speech possible. It has also been stated by some writers on the subject that in the great apes, the front of the vocal cords is covered by the epiglottis. This is said to hamper free vibration of the cords. But I do not believe this is, in fact, the case. In the apes the epiglottis is shorter and situated nearer the vocal cords and less crowded by the tongue than in man. It is difficult to see how this could prevent the use of those organs for speech, were these creatures otherwise capable of it. In the evolution of man, while the top of the skull has ballooned, the base of the skull has been squeezed and crowded. The oral cavity is short, wide, and deep, with a thick bulbous tongue. The back of the tongue is positioned nearer the epiglottis, and the larynx extends somewhat farther down the neck. The soft palate moves more freely than in the apes and is capable of closing off the oralpharynx from the naso pharynx. Man is believed to be the only animal capable of doing this. The soft palate may be controlled as a valve, at will, shunting noisy air away from the nasal passages and into the oral cavity where long drawn-out expiratory sounds can be chopped into meaningful speech units.[23]

Communication may be defined as any process of transmitting and receiving information, signals, or messages, whether by gesture, voice, or other means. It is the unit of the social situation. Language may be defined as any *system* of communication between animals. Speech may be defined as a verbal form of language which conveys information by chopping vocal tones into pulsations of discrete vibrating segments. Man alone can articulate such speech segments, and by means of his speech organs transmit symbols to others. Language is the formal code, the institution, the abstraction; speech is the message, the act. We *speak* a language according to the agreed, the formal, rules. The languages of man are mutually translatable, but the languages of animals are not—they are at most only interpretable.

Every muscle involved in speech is steered and controlled by spoken sounds. Because speech has to be learned by hearing the spoken sounds, those who are born deaf are unable to speak properly, if at all. They are deaf-mute. Intelligible speech requires the correlated activities of the larynx, pharynx, cheeks, mouth, tongue, and lips, activities which it takes years to learn. It used to be thought that there were special areas in the brain for speech, such as Broca's and Wernicke's, in the left frontal and temporal lobes respectively. It is now known that this is highly unlikely to be the case on theoretical, anatomical, and physiological grounds. Conrad[24] has resumed the evidence showing that damage to almost any part of the cortex of the brain can produce a loss of the ability to use language (aphasia). It has also been shown that Broca's area can sometimes be damaged without causing any such impairment.[25]

Hunting and the Origin of Speech

Under hunting conditions in cooperation with one's fellow-hunters the highest premium, as we have already said, would have been placed upon behavior calculated to achieve the desired end—the securing of the quarry. Such successful cooperative hunting would have been greatly facilitated were the hunters able to communicate by sound with their fellow-hunters. It would be highly desirable to transmit instantly information regarding changing intentions and strategies paralleling the changing conditions during the hunt. Different individuals, from their various angles of vision, would see and foresee behavior likely to yield the most favorable result, and would want to communicate this to their fellow-hunters, particularly over distances where gestures would be ineffective. The only way in which this could be satisfactorily achieved while running, and the running itself would facilitate such expiratory sounds, would be by meaningful vocalizations which conveyed to everyone what was required in order to meet the changing conditions which were either being observed or foreseen.

It has been repeatedly pointed out that during man's early evolution problem-solving abilities would have been at the highest premium. This would be especially so during the hunt. With the ability to interpret and imitate the meaningful cries of one's companions, such a combination of abilities would have had a high survival value. Thus, the development of tools, of intelligence, and of speech would have gone hand in hand. Those individuals having the ability to solve problems quickly and to interpret the expressions of others would be more likely to leave a progeny than those wanting in such a combination of abilities. Thus, speech, as well as toolmaking and intelligence, would have had the highest adaptive value.

In stalking and in chasing prey, speech would constitute an invaluable aid. It would, however, appear unlikely that speech first developed during the stalking phase of man's economic activities, for in stalking prey it is essential to be quiet, and under such conditions speech would not have developed, unless in the form of gestural or sign language. Gestural and sign language almost certainly accompanied rather than preceded spoken language, and has always remained an essential part of speech. Pantomime and the mimicking of sounds would often go together, as they do to this day. Most verbalized communication consists of a combination of articulate sound, voice, and gesture. Communication is often effective by the use of one or the other of these alone.

It is more likely that the stage of evolution during which speech developed corresponded with that phase of man's economic activities in which he moved on from a small-game collector to become an active hunter. *Zinjanthropus*, therefore, may not yet have developed speech, though it is possible that he developed the rudiments of speech at least, for toolmaking implies a degree of mental development which suggests the existence of a capacity for speech—however rudimentary that capacity and that speech may have been. It is more likely that the early hunters would attempt to make meaningful cries during the chase than during their collecting or simple stalking of small game. But even in the securing of small game a good deal of running was often necessary, although not as much as in hunting. In running, and in the excitement of the chase, there would be a strong tendency toward the violent expiration of sounds, which could readily be converted into a meaningful cry or yell. All that is necessary is the repetition and imitation of such sounds in similar contextual situations for them to become established as words. In this manner a simple vocabulary would come into being, which could then serve as a basis for further elaboration and development.

Speech was among the early tools originated by man during the early hunting phase of his evolution. Because of its high adaptive value as the medium through which cooperation is secured, speech has played a seminal role in man's evolution. That it originated under the pressure of necessity, and was preserved by natural selection, is in conformity with all that we know concerning the evolution of many of man's other traits. As Sophocles wrote:

Of all the wonders, none is more wonderful than man,
Who has learned the art of speech, of wind-swift thought,
And of living in neighborliness.

If we would seek for the one trait which separates man from all other animals, it is speech. Until a child can speak it acts like a young ape. When it is able to speak it acts like a human being. The difference in conduct is not due to any difference in age of any kind, but is intimately associated with the presence or absence of the ability to talk. A one-year-old child can solve most of the problems with which a chimpanzee is normally faced, and it is therefore said to be of "chimpanzee-age." But as soon as the child learns to talk, it makes rapid progress, and is soon way ahead of the ape. Speech bridges interhuman space. Words, their meanings, and interconnections, rapidly serve to organize the human world for the child in a manner impossible to the ape. Words, as symbols, serve as the repositories and transmitter mechanisms of the ideas, the wisdom, the traditions, and the culture of the group, for what cannot be directly perceived or tangibly felt, the child, through the stimulus of the word-symbols, can imagine, with a resulting expansion of his mental horizons. Speech is the means by which the raw material *Homo* is transformed into the finished article *sapiens*.

Speech is the most instrumental of the tools of intelligence. It is intelligence made explicit in the use of symbols largely for the attainment of practical ends. The meaning of a word is always the action it produces, the changes it effects. Speech is the organization of thought through symbols. Hence, the best way to the study of the thought of any people is through their language, for their language is the expression of their thought. We know nothing of the language of early man, but it was at first undoubtedly very simple, and largely limited to the achievement of practical ends. Probably in the course of later development *speculative* or *rational intelligence* gradually developed, a speculative or rational intelligence involving the organization of complex abstractions and systems of symbols, incorporated into and reflected by the character of the language. From its very origins the natural function of speech has always been to keep man in touch with his fellow man.

Brains, Genes, and Culture

Speech is, of course, a social activity, and as such it is the principal form of behavior through which human beings communicate. Man is not only a symbol user but also a symbol maker, and it is through the increasing complexity of his symbol making that he has achieved his present high technological development. With the creation and usage of organized systems of symbols man created a new dimension of experience which at the same time yielded him an increasing control over his environment. This new dimension of experience we call *culture*. Culture is man-made. It is the environment which man creates in order the better to control as much of the environment as he desires.

As the late Alfred Korzybski pointed out,[26] plants capture one kind of energy, convert it into another, and store it up; plants may therefore be described as belonging to the chem istry-binding class of life. Animals, being characterized by the faculty and freedom to move about in space, may therefore be defined as the space-binding class of life. Since he has the capacity to summarize, digest, and utilize the work, achievements, and experiences of the past for the benefit of the present and the progress of the future, man may therefore be said to belong uniquely to the time-binding class of life. This is an important series of distinctions, but man is much more than a time-binder—he is also a remarkable innovator. Nor is he simply a discoverer, one who finds out, but he is more than that, one who thinks up, devises or fabricates in the mind innovations which are original and novel. And this he does principally through the use of symbols. As he creates new symbols, his symbols create him. The process of symbol usage is called *symboling,* and a thing or event which is dependent upon symboling is called a *symbolate.* Symbolates acting in relation to one another are of the essence of culture. For example, my behavior in relation to my father is dependent upon a complex of symbols which I have learned which tell me how I must behave toward my father. That is behavior which has been culturally determined. The psychologist would be interested in how I feel about my father and the psychophysical sets I may have developed in relation to him, my organismic responses and their conditioning. Thus, when we study the cultural world it is from the standpoint of the universe of symbolates operating in relation to each other largely in an extraorganismic or extrasomatic context, whereas the same relationships between symbolates viewed from the standpoint of their functional relationships to the behavior of individuals and their motivations, in other words, in an organismal or somatic context, become psychological. Thus, the difference between the sciences devoted to the study of culture and psychology arises simply out of the difference in the focus of interest.[27]

Ideas, attitudes, acts, and objects have as a common factor the process of symboling, and there are three kinds of symbolates: (1) ideas and attitudes, (2) overt acts, and (3) material objects. The meanings of symbolates, it is important to note, can only be understood by human beings who have learned to translate them. And this is precisely what each culture enables its members to do according to its own specifications. In this way every member of a particular culture is custom-made, developed according to the pattern prevailing in that particular culture. Thus, culture has become man's principal means of adapting himself to the environment, and so, indeed, it was from the very beginning of man's early development. The difference in the culture of early man compared with that of later man lies only in the difference in complexity which characterizes some of the more technologically advanced human cultures compared with those of early man. Culture, then, consists of the things and events dependent upon symboling which the individual learns as an organized system of behavior, ideas, beliefs, attitudes, sentiments, acts, customs, codes, institutions, forms of art, speech, tools, implements, utensils, ornaments, fetiches, charms, and the like. Culture is a completely new zone of adaptation, a wholly new dimension into which man has moved, in which he creates and directs his own adaptation to the environment. The change over from tool using and occasional tool modification to toolmaking was the first of the steps which initiated the peculiarly human development of culture. The augmentation of plant gathering by the gathering of juvenile and slow-moving animals in the satisfaction of hunger represented a still further step in this cultural development. But it was not until the development of hunting, the actual chasing of game in cooperation with others, that the development of human culture and of the peculiarly human traits of man received its greatest stimulus.

Hunting does not appear to have received its proper due as a factor in contributing to the cultural and physical evolution of man. This is all the more interesting because it is in this manner that man earned his living for almost the whole of his history, only ceasing to do so in a few areas of the earth less than ten thousand years ago. Hunting always presents an enormous variety of challenges which call for all sorts of ingenious responses. Nothing puts so concentrated a pressure upon the hunter's imagination, resourcefulness, and inventiveness. Demands are made upon the faculties which lead to experiment, discovery, and invention—to the development of intelligence.

Intelligence is, of course, not only useful in the hunt, but is of highly generalized value. It is also the best defense against falling victim to other animals oneself. With intelligence to draw upon, neither natural nor artificial weapons are necessary. It is probable, then, that it was hunting that served as the selective pressure that gave the greatest encouragement to the development of human intelligence, and to the corresponding decline in the efficacy of instinct. The consequences of this are what made man increasingly human—for man's development as a human being has paralleled the development of each of his peculiarly human traits, the most all-embracing of which is culture.

The human brain is as large as it is because a creature that must learn and perform the required cultural skills of man must have a brain large enough to accommodate all the necessary neural elements. There are a prodigious number of these. There are probably more than ten billion neurons in the cortex of the brain alone, more than double the number in any ape brain.

When one compares size of brain with ability to solve complex problems in different related species, the species with the larger brains are found to be more proficient than those with the smaller brains.[28] A purely quantitative increase in the number of neurons and therefore in the size of the brain enables the organism to respond to a much wider range and finer detail of stimuli than would otherwise be possible. The increase in the number of neurons means that the number of associative connections between them will increase in geometric progression. This means a great increase in functional capacities and skills. The emphasis is on the *functional capacities and skills,* and this needs to be underscored, for it is to these traits that the size of the brain is most closely related. As Gerard points out, the size of the motor area of the brain, which controls various muscles, is not related to the size of the muscle but to the skill in using it.[29] The motor area for the tongue in the human brain is much larger, for example, than the whole motor area for the leg in the chimpanzee.

The role of toolmaking and tool using in the growth and development of the brain is reflected in the great enlargement of the hand area of the motor cortex of the brain. Allowing about thirty years to a generation, there have been about 65,000 generations since the australopithecines. The brain has increased during that time about two and one-half times in size. Compared with similar changes in other animal groups this rate of growth represents a very rapid selection rate.

The fossil evidence indicates that the rate of increase in the size of the brain in prehistoric man was quite rapid, culminating in a brain size of, on the average, 1550 cc. in Neanderthal man. This rate of growth suggests the action of strong selective pressures favoring genes for increased brain size. The average brain size of the human species since the day of Neanderthal man has stabilized itself at about 1400 cc., although in major groups such as the mongoloids brain size remains at about 1500 cc. The increasing self-domestication of man has possibly had the same effect in reducing brain size, a phenomenon observable in domestic animals. Domestic animals, while retaining the body weight of their wild counterparts, undergo a reduction in brain weight of about 20 per cent.[30] Considering the virtually explosive rate of growth of the brain in man, it will be of interest to inquire into the nature of the pressures which placed so high a selective value on genes for brain size.

TABLE III

AVERAGE CRANIAL CAPACITIES IN APES, AUSTRALOPITHE-
CINES, AND SOME FOSSIL AND LIVING
VARIETIES OF MEN (CC.)

Gibbon (*Hylobates*)	97
Siamang (*Symphalangus*)	125
Chimpanzee (*Pan*)	400
Orang-Utan (*Pongo*)	416
Gorilla (*Gorilla*)	543
Zinjanthropus boisei (Australopithecine)	530
Plesianthropus (Australopithecine)	506
Australopithecus africanus (Australopithecine)	600
Paranthropus robustus (Australopithecine)	650
Homo habilis	680
Australopithecus prometheus (Australopithecine)	715
Telanthropus capensis (Australopithecine)	850
Homo erectus (*Pithecanthropus*) *erectus* II	775
Homo erectus (*Pithecanthropus*) *robustus*	900
Homo erectus (*Pithecanthropus*) *erectus* I	940
Paranthropus crassidens (Australopithecine)	1,000
Homo erectus (*Sinanthropus*) *pekinensis*	1,043
Solo man	1,100
Steinheim	1,117
Saldanha	1,250
Australian aborigines (Northern Territory)	1,256
Rhodesian man	1,305
Bushman	1,329
Australian aborigines (Victoria)	1,338
Neanderthal	1,553

Changes in frequencies of genes are usually brought about through natural selection in adaptation to environmental challenges. The adaptive value of mental abilities is, in and of itself, insufficient to account for the rapid rate of brain growth in prehistoric man. While natural selection adapts the population to environmental changes, man performs this adaptation for himself by means of his mental abilities, in which, among other things, he selects the environment, and changes it to suit his purposes by cultural means. By producing such changes man correlatively produces the conditions which lead to those gene changes which are adapted to meet the challenges they present. Every new invention, every new discovery, had, as it were, a self-accelerating, an autocatalytic effect both upon the genetic and the cultural systems. It put a selective premium upon those who were able to take advantage of the new inventions and discoveries, and by both means facilitated further invention and discovery. Every cultural advance increased the selective advantage of those who were capable of utilizing it and of increasing the selective disadvantage of those who were incapable of using it. In this way the cultural pressures on the genetic evolution of man for increasing ability to adapt himself to the cultural environment have played a dominant role in the evolution of man. Without being aware of it man has produced the changing conditions of his own evolution,[31] and has been selecting himself increasingly in relation to the cultural zone of adaptation. It would seem clear, then, that in the evolution of man cultural and genetic changes have proceeded in an interactive positive feedback relation, that, as Caspari has put it, "genic changes have caused an increased ability for active adaptation by cultural means, and adaptation by cultural means has changed environmental conditions in such a way that different selective pressures have arisen, giving rise to further genetic changes in the population."[32] These two processes have interacted upon one another throughout the evolution of man, and continue to do so. Cultural evolution has not suppressed or supplanted genetic evolution, but interacts with the genetic system to produce both genetic and cultural change—but the adaptation, and the genetic changes, are now largely in relation to the cultural changes that man produces, for culture markedly affects the adaptive value of genes. Selective pressures have increasingly placed a premium upon genes for cultural competency. The characteristics of fitness now change from a genotype of fixed responses to a limited environment, to a genotype without fixed responses, but with the capacity to respond adaptively to a large range of environments.

Culture, then, represents a biological adaptation, based on genetic changes, but transmitted non-genetically, that is, through the socially interactive process of learning. Culture is man's social heredity. Within the limits set by the genes every *human* act of the organism is learned, acquired, through the action of the culture upon him. Though based on genetic factors which make it possible, culture is itself an extragenetic, a superorganic, system which functions in the service of man just as any tool does, to enlarge and extend the satisfaction of his needs.

Immaturity—Dependency

A creature that is required to learn as much as the human child must learn in order to function adequately as a human being must have a long learning period in which to do so. Human beings are characterized by a very long learning period, which lasts far beyond childhood. It has been a matter of interest that the human infant is also characterized by a prolonged period of immaturity, during which it cannot even move around for itself, far more prolonged than that of any other mammal. What can be the significance of this prolonged period of infant immaturity? Let us consider the facts.

The newborn elephant and the fallow deer can run with the herd shortly after they are born. By the age of six weeks, the infant seal has been taught by his mother to navigate his watery domain for himself. These animals all have long gestation periods, presumably because animals that give birth to small litters are unable to protect them as efficiently as predatory animals, and must, therefore, give birth to young who are in a fairly mature state. A long gestation period serves to allow for such maturation.

The elephant, which has a gestation period of 515 to 670 days, gives birth to a single infant. In animals such as the fallow deer, which give birth to a litter of two or three, the gestation period is 230 days. In the seal, which produces only a single pup at a birth, the gestation period varies from 245 to 350 days. Predatory animals, by contrast, are very efficient in protecting their young, and have a short gestation period.

The lion, for example, which generally has a litter of three pups, has a gestation period of 105 days. Man has a gestation period of 266½ days, which is distinctly in the class of long gestation periods. Since this is so, what can be the explanation for man's birth in so extremely immature a state?

Baby apes are also born in an immature condition, but remain in that state for a much shorter time than does the human infant. The gestation period in the gorilla is about 252 days, in the orang-utan 273 days, and in the chimpanzee 231 days. Labor in the apes generally lasts not more than two hours, as compared with an average of fourteen hours for the firstborn and eight hours for the later-born in the human female—we shall return to the possible significance of this difference shortly. As in man, one infant is usually produced, but compared with that of man the development of the young ape is somewhat more rapid, so that the infant ape takes about one-third to two-thirds of the time the human infant does to develop such traits as lifting the head, rolling, worming along, sitting alone, standing, and walking. It has been noted upon an earlier page that ape mothers tenderly care for their young for several years, and it is not uncommon for breastfeeding to continue for three or more years. Man's immaturity in infancy, therefore, may be regarded as an extension of the basic hominoid infant immaturity characteristic of all manlike forms. Among anthropoids the care, feeding, and protection of the young fall exclusively to the females. The males act to protect the females and the young only when they are endangered.

While the length of the gestation period is virtually within the same range in anthropoids and in man, there is a marked difference in the growth of the fetus in the two groups. This is seen in the great acceleration in the growth of the human compared with the anthropoid fetus toward the end of the gestation period. This is most clearly observed in the growth of the human fetal brain, which by the time of birth has acquired a volume of about 375 cc. to 400 cc. Total body weight of the human newborn averages 7 pounds. In the chimpanzee total body weight of the newborn is, on the average, 4⅓ pounds (1800 grams), and the brain volume is about 200 cc. In the gorilla the total body weight of the newborn is about 4¾ pounds (1980 grams), and brain size at birth would appear to be not much more than in the chimpanzee.[33]

The smaller size of the anthropoid newborn is to some extent probably correlated with the short duration of labor

TABLE IV

LENGTH OF GESTATION AND POSTNATAL GROWTH
PERIODS AND LIFE SPAN IN APE AND MAN

Genus	Gestation (days)	Menarche (years)	Eruption of first and last permanent teeth (years)	Completion of general growth (years)	Life span (years)
Gibbon	210	8.5	?–8.5	9	30
Orang-Utan	273	?	3.0–9.8	11	30
Chimpanzee	231	8.8	2.9–10.2	11	35
Gorilla	252	9.0	3.0–10.5	11	35
Man	266½	13.5	6.2–20.5	20	75

in the anthropoid female. However, in man the large body size, and especially the large size of the head at 266½ days of fetal age, necessitates the birth of the child at that time, for if it were not born then and it continued to grow at the rate at which it is organized to grow, it could not be born at all—with fatal consequences for the continuation of the human species.

As a result of the adoption of the erect posture the pelvis in both the human female and male has undergone major rearrangement in all its parts. Among these changes has been a narrowing in the pelvic outlet. During parturition, the pelvic outlet enlarges a little owing to the relaxation of the pelvic ligaments, enough to permit the head of the child, with a certain amount of compression, to pass through. In adaptation to this situation the skull bones of the human infant have grown so much less than those of the ape infant of the same gestation age, in relation to the membranes in which these bones develop, that a considerable amount of movement and overlapping is rendered possible in adaptation to the compressive forces that will act upon them during the process of birth. The human infant, then, is born when it is because it must be born at that time; otherwise the rapid rate at which its brain grows would make it impossible for it to be born in the ordinary way. The brain growth of the anthropoid infant presents no such problems, particularly in view of the mother's generous pelvic arrangements.

Not only does the prolonged period of behavioral immaturity of the human infant suggest that it is born in a most unready state, so also does its biochemical and physiological immaturity. For example, several of the enzyme systems which render later effective physiological functioning possible are undeveloped in the human infant. In this the human infant shares a trait not uncommon to those of a number of other mammals, except that in the human infant, unlike most other mammalian infants thus far investigated, most of these enzymes are not present at all. In guinea pigs and mice, for example, the liver enzymes develop during the first week of life, but require some eight weeks for full development. It appears that in all mammals some factor is present in the uterine environment which represses the formation of liver enzymes in the fetus.[34] In the human infant the liver enzymes do not appear to be fully developed until a good many months have passed.[35] Gastric enzymes are present which are fully capable of dealing with the ingested colostrum and milk from the maternal breast, but they cannot effectively metabolize foods normally consumed by older children.

Uterogestation and Exterogestation

All the evidence indicates that while the duration of the gestation period in man differs by only a week or two from that of the great apes, a large number of factors, all combining to lead to the much more prolonged development of the human infant, causes him to be born before his gestation has been completed. One would think that a creature developing at the rate of the human fetus in the later stages of uterine development and during childhood should, developmentally, enjoy a much longer period of gestation within the womb. After all, every one of the developmental periods is greatly extended in duration in man as compared with that in apes (Table IV); why not also the period of gestation? The reason principally is that the growth of the brain of the fetus is so rapid during the latter part of "gestation" and the mother's pelvis is so narrow, the fetus must be born when its head has reached the maximum size consonant with its passage through the birth canal. That is no mean accomplishment. Indeed, the passage through the four inches of the birth canal is the most hazardous journey a human being ever makes. The fact is, the human fetus is born before his gestation has been completed. The rate of growth of the brain is proceeding at such a pace that it cannot continue within the womb, and must continue outside it. In other words, the survival of the fetus and the mother requires the termination of gestation within the womb (uterogestation) when the limit of head size compatible with birth has been reached, and long before maturation occurs.

Gestation, then, is not completed by the process of birth, but is only translated from gestation within the womb (uterogestation) to gestation outside the womb (exterogestation). The limit of exterogestation in the human infant may be set at the stage of development of effective locomotion on all fours, that is, when the infant begins to crawl about for himself. The average duration of exterogestation lasts exactly the same time as the period of uterogestation, namely, 266½ days. In this connection it is also of interest to note that while the mother continues to nurse her infant, pregnancy will not usually occur for at least 266½ days after the birth of the child. Nursing the child at the breast suppresses ovulation, and thus constitutes a natural method of child-spacing. It also suppresses menstrual bleeding. Menstrual bleeding tends to be heavier and longer when a baby is not breastfed, and the mother's reserve energies tend, therefore, to be somewhat depleted. The premature cessation of breastfeeding would, then, result in distinct disadvantages, especially for a mother who already has other children to care for. Hence, breastfeeding not only confers advantages upon the baby but also upon the mother, and therefore upon the group. This is to mention only the physical advantages of breastfeeding. Even more important are the psychological advantages which are reciprocally conferred upon infant and mother in the nursing situation, especially in a species in which the mother is symbiotically designed to continue the gestation of her child outside the womb.

To learn what the child must learn in order to function as an adequate human being, he must, then, have a large brain. It is a striking fact that by the time the human child has attained its third birthday it has also virtually achieved the full adult brain size. Brain volume of the human three-year-old is 960 cc., while the brain volume of the human adult, attained at the age of 20 years, is 1200 cc.; that is to say, after the end of its third year the human brain will add only another 240 cc. to attain its full size, and that 240 cc. will accumulate by small accretions over the next 17 years. In other words, at the end of three years of age the human child has achieved 90 per cent of its brain growth. Significantly, the infant brain more than doubles in volume by the end of its first year to about 750 cc., or 60 per cent of its adult size. Almost two-thirds of the total growth of the brain is achieved by the end of the first year. It will take another two years to add almost another third to the volume attained at the end of the third year. (Table V.) In its first year, therefore, the infant's brain grows more than it will ever again in any one year.

It is important that most of the brain growth be accomplished during the first year, when the infant has so much to learn and do, for the first year of life requires a great deal of unobtrusive packing for a journey that will endure the rest of the traveler's life. To perform this packing successfully he must have a brain much larger than 375 to 400 cc., but quite clearly he cannot wait till he has grown a brain of 750 cc. before being born. Hence, he must be born with the maximum-sized brain possible, and do the rest of his brain growing after birth. Since the human fetus must be born when its

88   THE HUMAN REVOLUTION

TABLE V
Growth in Brain and Cranial Capacity, Both Sexes

Age	Weight (gm.)	Volume (cc.)	Cranial capacity (cc.)
Birth	350	330	350
3 months	526	500	600
6 months	654	600	775
9 months	750	675	925
1 year	825	750	1,000
2 years	1,010	900	1,100
3 years	1,115	960	1,225
4 years	1,180	1,000	1,300
6 years	1,250	1,060	1,350
9 years	1,307	1,100	1,400
12 years	1,338	1,150	1,450
15 years	1,358	1,150	1,450
18 years	1,371	1,175	1,475
20 years	1,378	1,200	1,500

Source: *Growth and Development of the Child,* Part II, White House Conference, Century Co., New York, 1933, p. 110.

brain has reached the limit of size compatible with its admission and extrusion through the birth canal, such maturation or further development as other mammals complete before birth the human mammal will have to complete after birth. In other words, the gestation period will have to be extended beyond birth.

The human infant is almost, if not quite, as immature at birth as the little marsupial which, born in an extremely immature state, finds its way into its mother's pouch, there to undergo its exterogestation until it is sufficiently matured. The human infant remains immature much longer than the infant kangaroo or opossum, but whereas the marsupial infant enjoys the protection of its mother's pouch during its period of immaturity, the human infant is afforded no such advantage. However, the human infant constitutes part of a symbiotic unit; the mother, having given it shelter and sustenance within the womb, is fully equipped to continue to do so outside the womb, at least as efficiently as the marsupial mother is for her young. The biological unity, the symbiotic relationship, maintained by mother and conceptus throughout pregnancy does not cease at birth; indeed, it is naturally designed to become even more intensively functional and interoperative after birth than during uterogestation.

To put the preceding discussion of infant brain volume in proper perspective, it should be observed that while an adult cranial capacity of 1400 cc. was not achieved by man until a stage of his development later than the australopithecine, the forms of man that immediately followed the australopithecines undoubtedly had larger brains than they. The pithecanthropines of Java and China had an adult cranial capacity of about 950 cc. In any event, the narrowing of the pelvis in the small post-australopithecines, whoever they were, and in the australopithecines themselves, together with the increasing size of the brain in the late fetus, would have presented much the same problems as those that were discussed in the light of the conditions we know to prevail in modern forms of man. A two-year-old pithecanthropine, *Homo erectus robustus* from the Lower Pleistocene of Modjokerto in East Java, indicates that the infant pithecanthropine already had a comparatively large brain in relation to adult brain size. Whatever the brain volume of early infant man may have been, the preceding discussion is believed to apply in general to the conditions that prevailed among early man. It should be remembered that both body size and weight in early man were less than they grew to be in later forms of man, and that therefore it is always the size of the brain in relation to body size (and weight) which must be borne in mind in comparing brain sizes of early man with those of later, larger forms of man.

Natural Selection and Maternity

Among the apes and man not only does the process of coitus have to be learned, but so does the art of being a mother. It has many times been observed that with her firstborn the ape mother, especially in captivity, is bewildered and does not

understand what has happened or what to do with the newborn. This is also likely to be true with very young mothers
of the human species.[36] Thus, not only is a certain amount of
physiological maturity necessary before a female is able to
reproduce, but a certain amount of psychological maturity,
implying learning, is also required before she can adequately
mother an infant. The maturation of the physiological and
psychological processes necessary for the satisfactory comple-
tion of the birth and nursing of a child is a slow one in the
human species. The first menstruation (menarche), which
occurs at about 13.5 years in the human female, is not co-
incident with the ability to reproduce, but represents only a
beginning puberal phase in a long extended process of physiological development. From menarche to maturity, when the
female becomes optimally capable of bearing and caring for
a child, a period of eight years, on the average, elapses. During
this maturation period the female learns a great deal about the
care of children. In almost all nonliterate societies today, and
this was almost certainly so among the populations of early
man, the female was usually married immediately after the
appearance of menarche. Since ovulation does not normally
occur, on the average, until three years have elapsed after
menarche, most females would enjoy an extended period
during which to learn the social techniques of motherhood.
The female, however, also inherits capacities which under the
proper stimulation will respond to all the needs of the dependent infant. These responses are in part constitutionally
based and in part learned. The constitutional or genetic basis
of these responses represents the culmination of 75 million
years of mammalian development, and stands in the direct
line of descent of the constitutional determinants of maternal
behavior in man's anthropoid ancestors, to a large extent
closely resembling that which we observe among our living
anthropoid relations. However, in the human species, there
has undoubtedly been a process of social and natural selection
of those females possessing the necessary traits likely to contribute to the survival of so precariously dependent a creature
as the human newborn. These traits would be both behavioral
and physical.

The behavioral traits may be best resumed by the word
"love." Love is defined as behavior calculated to confer survival benefits in a creatively enlarging manner upon the dependent child. The tenderness toward the child, the deep
involvement in its well-being, and all those other qualities a

loving mother exhibits toward her child, have undoubtedly been at a high premium in the evolution of the human species. These profoundly important qualities of the mother have been recognized most beautifully in an old Talmudic saying, which has it that since God could not be everywhere he created mothers. The critical position in which the mother stands in relation to the child could hardly be better described.

That the relationship between infant and mother from the moment of birth is fundamental for the subsequent social development of the individual has been abundantly demonstrated both by investigation and everyday observation. The complexity of the interacting symbiotic relationship in the exterogestative period between mother and child constitutes a miracle of reciprocal interchange of benefits. Not only does the loving mother minister to all the needs of her child, but the child in return confers many benefits upon the mother. It is not simply the infant who has a great need of continuing support from its mother after birth, but the mother has, in a complementary manner, an equally great need to continue to support and to give succor to the child. Giving birth to the child deepens and reinforces the mother's interest in its welfare. Her whole organism has been readied to minister to its needs, to nurse it at the breast. In nursing, the infant ingests the beneficial colostrum, which lasts for the first four days and which contains gamma globulins that confer passive immunities upon the infant, until it acquires its own active immunities. Nursing also confers benefits upon the mother. Contractions of the uterus, which initiate return of the womb to normal size, produce constriction of the blood vessels, and thus reduce the postpartum hemorrhage, cause detachment of the placenta, and complete the third stage of labor by the ejection of the placenta. The psychophysiological benefits which, in the continuing symbiotic relationship, mother and child reciprocally confer upon one another are vitally important for their future development as human beings.

The Breast

Among the many changes that resulted from the adoption of the erect posture and the new way of life was the development of the female breast. The breast of the human adolescent and mature female is of unique form among the primates. In the New and Old World monkeys, and among the great

apes, the breast of the female, during pregnancy and lacta-
tion, may enlarge appreciably, but in the nonpregnant state
remains comparatively flat. By contrast, the form of the breast
in the human female is usually well developed at adolescence,
and while flat-breasted human females occasionally occur,
these are the exceptions, the greater number of females usually
possessing breasts of substantial size.

The unique form of the human breast, in all the varieties
it exhibits, has been attributed to sexual selection. This explanation is, however, difficult to accept because in prehistoric
populations it is unlikely that females would have been
selected on any ground other than their availability. Prehistoric populations were very small, of the order of a few
score or a few hundred. With such population numbers, as we
know from existing small societies, marriage tends to be
strictly regulated. The individual is not free to choose his
future spouse; this is predetermined by the existing marriage
rules. Marriage tends to become free only when the population increases in size. In small nonliterate societies marriage
is usually strictly regulated, and this was almost certainly the
case in prehistoric societies. From this it would follow that
if selection of mates was not permitted, then sexual selection
can have played no role in the evolution of human traits.

It is much more likely that a number of other factors were
at work in producing the form of the human breast, chief
among these, probably, was the form of the suckling infant's
face. In the ape infant the jaws become quite projecting, a
condition called prognathism, but in the human infant the jaws
have grown so small they have been, as it were, retracted, so
that they are now situated in a plane virtually beneath the
orbits. As the jaws of the infant of early man became smaller
the female breast would become larger, for an infant with
retracted jaws would have considerable difficulty in suckling
at an undeveloped breast. Flat-breasted women tend to present
greater nursing problems than do full-breasted women. In
sucking, a baby does not grasp the nipple with its lips, but
rather the areolar region around it. In order to do so effectively, the upper lip, and sometimes the lower one also, is
equipped with a median suctorial papilla. In contrast to the
thin lips of the ape, the everted lips of the human infant are
clearly adapted for grasping a projecting hemisphere. Babies
presented with anything less are unlikely to suckle as well as
those presented with the appropriately shaped organ. This
is well brought out in an account given by von Allesch of an

infant chimpanzee's attempts at suckling as late as a week after birth. Von Allesch writes:

Finding the breast, continued however for "a long time" a difficult problem. The infant sought for the nipple with open mouth, at first by means of head movements alone, the remainder of the body continuing in its customary relation to the mother. These movements of the head were not for several weeks made purposeful, but the head with open mouth was turned aimlessly on all sides. Even when the young one accidentally touched the nipple with its hand, it was no guide. The mouth might be within a centimeter of its objective, yet no evidence of definite directive influence appeared. Odor seemingly did not aid.[37]

Von Allesch went on to point out that even long after this the infant's attempts to find the mother's breast were often fruitless. With a full-breasted female as mother this could hardly have been the case. A fully developed hemispherical or dependent breast would seem to have a selective advantage in that it enables the human newborn to complete the process of learning to suckle rather more quickly than it would at a flat breast.

Why, if the human type of female breast has so high a selective advantage, did not the anthropoids develop similar breasts? Apparently the selection pressures for such a development were quite different, and much greater in man, than in the anthropoids. The fact is that such well-developed breasts do occasionally occur among lactating apes, but when they do they are seldom as well developed as in the average lactating human female. The projecting jaws of the infant ape will, in general, do better at a comparatively undeveloped breast than would the reduced-jawed human infant. Furthermore, it is a question whether in a forest environment well-developed breasts would not constitute something of a handicap to the female.

Another factor that may possibly have played a role in the establishment of the form of the human breast is the ease with which the infant can find it. Although the mother usually helps the infant find the breast, this is much more efficiently achieved with a developed breast than with an undeveloped one. As we have seen, a newborn baby has to learn to suckle, and though he may learn to do so very quickly it would seem clear that he would learn to do so more easily at a fully developed breast than at a comparatively undeveloped one. Everted lips presenting sensitive mucous membranes would also be better adapted for this purpose than would thin lips. The speed with which a baby begins to suckle would not infrequently make all the difference between survival or not, not alone of the infant, but also of the mother. The baby receives the much-needed colostrum which serves, among other things, to activate the gastrointestinal tract as well as the genitourinary tract, and the mother experiences, among other things, those massive uterine contractions and the vaso-constriction of the uterine vessels which serve to reduce the postpartum hemorrhage, initiate the return of the uterus to normal size, and complete the third stage of labor, with the detachment and ejection of the placenta. These are vitally necessary changes in the postpartum period, and any organ which by its form would assist in the initiation of such changes would be of considerable adaptive value and would be most likely to confer survival benefits upon the possessors of such organs. Such individuals would be likely to leave a larger progeny than those not so characterized.

The female human breast, then, almost certainly owes its peculiar shape to natural selection, to the physiological bene-fits associated with its form, rather than to any sexually selective factors. For the immature human infant what better promise could there be of good things to come than being put to nurse at its mother's breast as soon as it is born, as is done in most nonliterate societies to this day? Birth for the human infant is the culmination of a prolonged series of disturbing experiences, some assuagement of which is the first of the fulfillments of his birthright which the infant has a biologic, a natural, right to expect.

The Significance of Prolonged Labor and Labor Pains

In the human species labor generally lasts about 14 hours with the first child, and some eight hours with later-born children, as compared with about two hours in apes. What can be the meaning of this long period of labor in the human species? It is suggested here that the explanation is to be found in the extended duration of the exterogestative period for which the uterogestative organism must be adequately prepared. A species with either no or a short exterogestative period requires either no real labor or a labor of only a short duration; preparation for postnatal functioning need be of the most minimal kind. In the case of the human infant there are many changes which must be induced in him, if he is to be adequately prepared to negotiate successfully the world of his immediate exterogestative existence, and for this a considerable time must elapse before the process of preparation has been completed. The process of birth forms the bridge between prenatal and postnatal life. It is a phase, a segment, of the continuum of individual development. The events of the birth process are designed to assist the newborn to adjust successfully to the next series of events in the developing continuum of its life. What the newborn must be prepared to deal with is the multiplicity of environmental stimulations, all of a new kind, to which he will be exposed immediately following birth, and then the next few days, weeks, and months of gradual adjustment and habituation to the requirements of exterogestative existence. Toward that end the newborn must be readied in all his sustaining systems, the respiratory, digestive, eliminative, nervous, and endocrine systems.

The prolonged contractions of the uterus not only prepare the fetus for, and finally accomplish, its expulsion from the womb, but also provide a massive total stimulation of the skin of the fetus. The purpose of this skin stimulation is to activate the sustaining systems in readiness for their postnatal functioning. The systems most especially involved are the digestive, eliminative, and respiratory systems. Among mammals generally immediately after the infant is born and for a considerable time thereafter the mother licks it with a single-minded devotion to her task which is striking. Most of the licking occurs in the anogenital (perineal) region. But the whole body is usually treated in the same manner. It for long seemed to be a satisfactory explanation that the mother was "washing" her young. The true explanation however is much deeper than that. Mammalian mothers lick their young in response to a complex of odor, dampness, and similar stimuli. The effect of the licking upon the young is to activate their digestive and eliminative systems and to stimulate their respiratory functions, for if the animals are not licked they will die of failure of the eliminative systems to function.[38]

Human mothers do not lick their young. They do not need to, because the prolonged contractions of the uterus upon the skin of the fetus thoroughly accomplish the purposes which licking performs in other mammals. Prematurely delivered and cesarean delivered infants who have not enjoyed much skin stimulation in this way exhibit, it is interesting to note, a significantly greater incidence of respiratory and eliminative system disorders than do normally born children.[39] The indications are that the massive stimulation of the skin produced by the contracting uterus serves to activate or assists in the activation of the gastrointestinal and genitourinary tracts, as well as the respiratory tract. The peripheral sensory nerves in the skin are stimulated, these conduct the nerve impulses thus initiated to the central nervous system where, at the proper levels, they are mediated through the autonomic nervous system to the viscera which they innervate. Another function of prolonged labor may be to produce a permanent registration in the infant brain of an original anxiety state, which is consolidated by the separation from the mother by birth. There is now a good deal of evidence in support of this theory, as there is for the theory of the trauma of birth associated with the name of Freud's colleague Otto Rank. The function of both experiences being to reinforce the need to be appropriately anxious as a defense against dangerous situations when they arise.[40]

The Adaptive Value of Labor Pains

While there is much individual variation, labor pains are usually of the severest kind. It may well be that much of this pain is subjective, but it is nonetheless felt for all that. Stories to the effect that women in labor in nonliterate societies do not experience pain have proven to be untrue wherever it has been possible to check the facts. Careful studies, however, in this connection are woefully lacking. Anthropologists, wherever they have inquired into the matter, have always found that pain was associated with labor, however short the duration of labor. In the female ape, in the later stages of labor at least, pain appears to be experienced, and this also seems to be the case in many other mammals. The human female is not unique, therefore, in experiencing pain during labor. What does appear to be unique in the human female is the intensity of the pains experienced and the length of time over which they are extended. Even Marais, who carefully observed baboons under natural conditions, and who states that no other animal undergoes greater birth pains, agrees that in the human female labor pains reach the highest intensity.[41] Many experienced authorities believe that labor pains in the human female are in most cases subjective. Whether this is so or not, there is good evidence that labor is in many cases made painful by the fear, anxiety, mystery, and pain with which the whole process of birth is so frequently surrounded.

In any event, whether objectively or subjectively based, or both, the pain is often there and it is a very real phenomenon.

For a human infant to survive under the conditions prevailing during the greater part of man's evolutionary history, the group as a whole had to be involved in contributing to the survival of the newly arrived infant, just as, in a very real continuing sense, the group (society) is involved today. The modern father's anxious pacing of the hospital corridor while his wife is in labor is no novel development. In virtually every society the father engages in propitiatory rites calculated to ensure a safe delivery, while in the same connection practices designed to control and mitigate anxiety are well-nigh universal. The long-extended pains associated with labor in the human female serve to impress upon everyone the cost at which a human being is brought into the world, the precariousness of human life, the thinness of the thread by which it hangs, and the value, therefore, of the life that is born.

Conception is easily produced, but the production of a human being must not be so easy if the human being is to be properly valued. The precariousness of his situation during parturition and the difficulty with which he is born serve to emphasize, as nothing else could, the preciousness as well as the tenuousness of human life. Hence, the adaptive value of pain associated with labor. Among other things, prolonged labor serves to impress upon everyone the value of the individual about to be born, so that he may be cherished and respected. Biologically this is a most important function to perform in a species in which one highly immature child is usually born at a time. The duration and the pain associated with labor ensure a focus of attention upon the impending event which would constitute an invaluable trait in a species in which the infant is dependent for its survival for as long a period as is the young of humankind.

In other words, since pain, subjective or otherwise, generally serves as a signal of danger to the individual, wherever in the body it occurs, it is necessary and desirable that some attention should be paid to the meaning of the pain. Pain, therefore, in childbirth, whether biologically, socially, or interactively conditioned, may have had a high selective value by causing attention to be concentrated upon its meaning, and upon the care of the newborn. Almost every human group has surrounded birth with mystery, ritual, ceremony, and excitement. The social functions of this are reasonably evident: to welcome with proper solemnity the new member of the group, to emphasize his worth, to propitiate the spirits, and to give thanks to the powers that have made possible the safe, if not uneventful, journey of the new arrival. At the same time these social practices, by focusing so much attention upon the value of the newborn, have made socially mandatory the care bestowed upon him, and have thus served to contribute to his survival. In such ceremonial and ritual practices may be perceived something of the high selective value which culture constitutes for the individual and the group. Just as our contemporary medical services have served to more than double the life expectancy of the individual, so the results of the ceremonial and ritual practices of early man served to contribute to his survival.

If labor pains have in fact served a useful purpose in the past, it is difficult to see what useful purpose they serve today.

Communication and Cooperation

Communication, Crying, and Weeping

The human infant has many needs which require satisfaction. In order to communicate those needs to others, he has no language but a cry. It was Tennyson who wrote:

> An infant crying in the night:
> An infant crying for the light:
> And with no language but a cry.

Were the infant's needs adequately satisfied at all times, it is highly probable he would not cry at all. There is no sound so compelling as the cry of the dependent infant, and there is little doubt that this development in the human infant was soon followed by another, namely, weeping.

It is a curious fact that man is the only creature that weeps —weeping being defined as the shedding of tears during emotional distress. Weeping has been attributed to other animals, but the fact is that psychic weeping is not known to occur as a normal function in any creature other than man. Students of the primates have uniformly failed to observe anything resembling weeping in any nonhuman primate. The great student of primate behavior, the late Dr. Robert Yerkes, wrote: "Young anthropoid apes frequently cry under certain circumstances which would induce like response in the human infant or child, but never in such instances even when the response is extreme have I seen tears."[42]

The age at which human infants begin to cry with tears varies considerably. Some infants are able to do so at or shortly after birth, and others fail to do so until they are 8 weeks of age.[43] The average age at which tears begin to accompany emotional crying is between 5 and 6 weeks. The peak of the ability to weep is reached in infancy and childhood, between 6 and 9 years, and gradually tapers off in adulthood. The late development of weeping in the human infant would suggest that it is a trait which developed some time after the assumption of hominid status. What factor or combination of factors, then, was it in the evolution of early man that may have been responsible for the appearance of weeping?

The length of the dependency period of the human child immediately suggests itself. During the earlier part of that dependency period, the human infant is without speech or the ability to help himself. His principal means of attracting the attention of others when he is in distress is by crying. Crying is essentially an activity involving the respiratory system and glottis, the muscle systems subserving these, the facial muscles, changes in arterial blood pressure, central nervous system changes, and changes in metabolism and the loss of heat. Babies cry with their eyelids firmly closed. The harder they cry the firmer the closure of the eyelids. The function of this is to oppose the pressure of the conjunctival and deeper vessels of the eye. For if the pressure of the eyelids is for some reason prevented or relaxed, there are likely to be breakages in the small vessels, such as may occur in sudden explosive coughs, sneezing, and even in yawning and laughter.

Even a short session of tearless crying in a young infant is likely to have a desiccating effect upon the mucous membranes of the nose and throat. This can be easily determined by examining the appearance of these mucous membranes in such infants compared with the mucous membranes of infants who cry with tears. The former appear to be excessively dry, ciliary action appears to have ceased, and there is considerable congestion of vessels with obvious breakages in some.

Excessive intake and expulsion of air even in adults will quickly dry mucous membranes, and it is this intake and expulsion of air in the tearless crying infant that I see as closely associated with the origin and the development of weeping.

The mucous membrane begins at the entrance of the nose and lines the structures of the nasal cavity and throat. The mucous membrane is lined with many ciliated cells, as well as with glands which produce a watery fluid and mucus, the latter containing an important enzyme called lysozyme. The hairlike processes (cilia) of the ciliated cells are in a continuous state of wavelike motion. The secretions of the glands and cells of the mucous membrane together form a protective investment over the air passages down to the ends of the bronchial divisions of the windpipe. By virtue of the underlying ciliary action the secretions of these glands move in the mucus matrix as a continuous blanket from the nose down the throat, where it is then swallowed and passes into the stomach.

It is the mucous membrane of the nose that constitutes the most immediate contact of the respiratory system with the external world. No other living cells are so directly exposed to the insults and assaults of the environment. The nasal mucous membrane must withstand the impact of respired air laden with viruses, bacteria, dust, particles, and gases. Discharges from the eye entering by the nasolacrimal ducts trickle back over the mucous membrane. The air may be dry or moist, it may be at subzero temperature or very hot, and changes in temperature of the respired air may vary rapidly from hot to cold. The mucous membrane is adapted to meet all these contingencies. Dry air deprives the mucus of its water content and impairs its efficiency as a continuously moving protective blanket.

By being dried with a jet of air the mucous membrane can be inactivated within a few minutes, and death of the ciliated cells can thus be produced. The bactericidal and bacteriostatic efficiency of the mucous membrane is considerable. It has been observed, for example, that 90 to 95 per cent of viable bacteria placed on the nasal mucous membrane are inactivated in from five to ten minutes.[44] Bacteria placed in contact with nasal secretions outside the body were much less effectively dealt with. More than twenty years ago Burnet observed that nasal mucus inactivates poliomyelitis virus of every type in vitro. The bacteriolytic action of the nasal secretions is principally due to the enzyme lysozyme.

When, for any reason, drying is produced in the mucous membrane, the cilia tend to lose their function and soon die.

This is followed by a piling up and drying of mucus and permeability of the mucous membrane. In this state the gelatinous mass of mucus constitutes a most hospitable culture medium for bacteria, which may then in large numbers easily pass through the permeable nasal mucosa. The consequences of this are not infrequently lethal.

It is proposed here that in early man weeping established itself as a trait of considerable adaptive value, in that it served to counteract the effects of more or less prolonged tearless crying upon the nasal mucosa of the infant. The dependent infants of early man who cried for prolonged periods of time within the first eighteen months of their lives, or even over a more extended period of time, without benefit of tears would stand less chance of surviving than those who cried with tears. Dry crying is dangerous because it renders the organism vulnerable to the invasion of harmful bacteria, and probably viruses, through a dried-out mucous membrane, the autosterilizing functions of which have been impaired. Crying with tears, on the other hand, serves to keep the mucous membrane wet and to assist in maintaining as well as reinforcing its functions.

Tears contain, among other things, a highly important enzyme elaborated by the lacrimal glands in high concentration, namely lysozyme, which we have already seen is also secreted by the mucous glands of the nasal mucosa. Lysozyme is highly bactericidal, that is, it speedily kills bacteria by dissolving their external coats. It is a fact of great interest that lysozyme is more concentrated in the tears of man than in the tears of any other of the higher mammals in which it is present. Many investigators have demonstrated that lysozyme is highly effective in inactivating viruses of various kinds. Lysozyme, then, constitutes an anti-infective protein of considerable value. This action of lysozyme in the human organism indicates one of the probable functions of weeping, especially in the infant and child, namely, as a physiologically protective device against the depredations of potentially noxious organisms. In addition, it should be mentioned that tears contain sugar and proteins of other kinds which are nutritional both to the eye and the nasal and associated membranes. Weeping, furthermore, activates the mucosa, increasing the blood supply and causing the mucosal glands to secrete additional lysozyme.

Weeping, then, very probably originated as an adaptively valuable trait in a species in which the crying of the young is extended over a much longer period of time than in any other species, as a protective adjustment against damage to the nasal mucous membrane of the young and the consequent reduction in fitness. Furthermore, it seems likely that early in the development of man those individuals were naturally selected for survival who were able to produce an abundant flow of tears, since the tears acted as a preventive of mucosal dehydration, whereas those who were not so able would be more likely to succumb more frequently at all ages and leave the perpetuation of the species to those who could weep.

It should be mentioned that the lacrimal gland does not secrete tears unless stimulated by emotion or a physical irritant. The lacrimal gland can remain nonfunctional or be removed without affecting the normal functioning of the eye, but weeping is not possible. The accessory glands (of Krause and Wolfring) which are situated in the upper and middle parts of the orbital (inner) surface of the eyelid, the conjunctival (goblet cell) glands which are situated on the membrane covering the inner surfaces of the eyelids and are reflected from them onto the eyeball, and the secretions of the meibomian glands, also on the inner lower surface of the eyelid, together combine to form a tear-film which keeps the eyes and eyelids and the eyeball moist and assists free movement of the eyelids upon the eyeballs. Hence, lacrimal secretion would not be necessary in the absence of weeping. In man the lacrimal glands are very well developed, and their size indicates that they have for long served a useful function. Females secrete greater quantities of lacrimal fluid than males, and even their teardrops are larger.

From the crying without to the crying with tears there eventually develops the weeping of sympathy. Such sympathetic weeping is a social response. The universality of the capacity to weep in the human species indicates the deep-seated biological basis of this behavioral trait. At the same time it indicates the existence of a profound biological basis for the feeling of sympathy which elicits the weeping. Indeed, at every point, at every stage, and in every sector of man's history the outstanding characteristic which he appears most to have been called upon to exhibit is this trait of sympathy, of fellow-feeling, of cooperation.

Laughter

Man is the only animal that laughs. Why? And what is the

function of that "happy convulsion," as someone has called it?

We are not short of theories to explain the mystery. Thomas Hobbes, in the 17th century, said that the "passion of laughter" arises from a "sudden conception of some eminency in ourselves" which accrues to us "by comparison with the infirmities of others." Later, in the early 20th century, Bergson theorized that the function of laughter was intimidation by humiliation. Nietzsche had taken the opposite view, suggesting that we laugh in order that we should not cry. William McDougall held that "laughter is primarily and fundamentally the antidote of sympathetic pain," and its biological function is "defence of the organism against the many minor pains to which man is exposed. . . ." Psychologist J. C. Gregory finds the function to be "enlightenment," that is to say, "relief." Max Eastman makes out as good a case as any for the notion that laughter may be a response to any pleasant stimulus, and to any unpleasant one that can be taken playfully.

Almost every theory has been concerned either with the structure or the function of laughter, while relatively few have been devoted to the question of the origin. Here I propose to offer a theory which, so far as I am aware, has not previously been proposed. If, in addition to novelty, the theory has any merit, the merit lies perhaps in fitting both the requirements of evolutionary theory and the findings of contemporary psychosomatic medicine.

Laughter is defined as an emotional response, expressive normally of joy, involving characteristic sounds of the voice and movements of the features and the body. The joy may take the form of mirth, amusement, ridicule, and so on.

Those of us who have observed chimpanzees under various favorable conditions feel quite confident that the chimpanzee exhibits behavior which looks very much like a primitive precursor of human laughter. Under certain conditions of obvious elation, or when tickled, the juvenile chimpanzee certainly looks as if he is engaging in something resembling soundless laughter. But this is behavior elicited in a human context. It is not known, and it is greatly to be doubted, whether chimpanzees under natural conditions indulge in such behavior. But whether they do or not, the fact that under any conditions an ape is capable of behavior which is even a primitive precursor of laughter is of more than passing interest, for it indicates that early man probably did not have to start, as it were, from scratch.

The suggestion I am going to make here is that those animals alone are capable of laughter who are alone capable of speech. Man being the only animal who speaks is therefore the only animal that laughs.

What is the association of laughter with speech? The suggestion is that laughter originated along with, more or less, the origin and evolution of speech as a kind of quasi-verbalized social expression of pleasure. As a result of the development of speech, that is the verbal expression of symbols and symbol relations, the occasions producing the sudden experiences of pleasure, of "sudden glory," would greatly multiply. The breaking of the sound barrier, as it were, would enable early man to express in full voice what the anthropoid could not express in the same way, firstly because of the infrequency of situations producing similar pleasurable states as those occurring in man, and secondly because of the anthropoid's lack of speech.

In 1947 Professor Theodosius Dobzhansky and I proposed the hypothesis that in the evolution of man the trait that was from the very beginning, and throughout the greater part of human history, at the highest premium, was the ability to get along with one's fellows, the trait of plasticity, flexibility, malleability, or educability. This hypothesis was proposed on the basis of what is known to transpire in virtually every society, in order to explain how it has come about that the average mental capacities of the so-called "races" of mankind are so very much alike. Having considered this question we concluded that there had been no significant differentiation of mental abilities in the different ethnic groups or "races" because special abilities were not given any particular preference over the long period of man's evolution.

The evidence, on the other hand, seemed unequivocally to indicate that the one ability that was continuously valued, whatever form the preferred behavior might temporarily assume, was the ability to get along with others.

This hypothesis has been favorably received by most scientists, and reference is being made to it here in order not merely to suggest that the "good mixer" has a long and honorable history, but that the individual who was able to communicate his "sudden glories" in an expressive manner would certainly enjoy social advantages over those who were less able or inclined to feel or to express their feelings that way. Even today, the "coefficient of risibility," as it might be called, varies considerably from individual to individual. Those who possessed the ability to express their pleasurable states in what we may now call laughter would tend to be socially preferred over those who were not so capable. In other words, those who tended to laugh would be socially selected and would thus enjoy advantages over those who were not as able to do so.

Social selection would in itself be sufficient to establish laughter as a capacity among all or nearly all human beings. Those, in short, who spoke their laughter were socially selected in preference to those who did not.

Everyone likes a good laugher. He brings good cheer with him wherever he goes; the very thought of him makes life more bearable. It is not for nothing that even today our highest paid entertainers should be not tragedians but comedians. Laughter is infectious, and most of us go out of our way to acquire the infection. We cannot think that it was otherwise in the earlier days of man's evolution, and if that was indeed so, then it would follow that the capacity to laugh would tend to become increasingly distributed as a trait common to all men. One, moreover, that exercised an increasingly humanizing effect upon man.

Laughter is essentially an interactive, a social, phenomenon, in which interacting persons reciprocally engage. Whatever contributes to such social reciprocity tends to exercise a humanizing effect, especially when there is an increasing humanization of the occasions upon which one laughs. It is, for example, no longer permissible, as it was in Hobbes's day, to laugh at the infirmities of others. The risible and the ridiculous change with the times. What we laugh at is to a large extent culturally determined. It is not the custom of the western world to respond to the reprimand of a superior with a smile, but it is in Japan. Movie stars should smile or laugh in their photographs, but professors should look serious. Again, the social function of laughter is underscored.

Let us now proceed to the second stage of our hypothesis: consider the manner in which natural selection would operate to favor those able to express their pleasurable states in laughter as compared with those not so able.

It is well known that laughter has a tonic effect. It is good for the health. It suffuses the organism with a feeling of well-being which virtually nothing else is comparably able to do. It refreshes and enlivens. It relieves and enlightens. It renders all burdens bearable, and brightens every prospect. It is like the sun, a "sudden glory," casting light and warmth all about it.

Physiologically, this "happy convulsion" involves the whole body, since the action of the diaphragm and trunk muscles produces a bellows-like action of the lungs resulting in an accelerated intake and output of air. The effect of this is a greater oxygenation of the blood, more efficient circulation, and the experiencing of the freshening effect. Involuntarily, laughter has the effect of good voluntary exercise, since virtually every part of the body is involved.

The psychophysiological effects of laughter would quite obviously confer survival benefits upon laughers and negatively select the non-laughers for survival. In this manner, in the course of time, laughter would become established throughout the human species as a function of biological value, as one with considerable psychological and social value.

Just as the development of speech has been an indispensable factor in the development of man's capacity to think and establish a mastery of his environment, so speech has been, it is here suggested, the basic condition in the development of man's capacity to laugh.

Finally, how shall we account for the convulsive nature of hearty laughter? Here, perhaps, we need appeal to no more than the fact that the kind of nervous excitation experienced during laughter is likely to overflow, irradiate into many segments of the body, resulting in reflex muscular, glandular and other changes, among them tearing from the eye and nose-blowing—all of which changes have very definite physiological functions, namely, to assist the more rapid respiration and to prevent the mucous membranes of nose and throat from becoming dehydrated as a result of the rapid respiration.

And at last: Why the loud noises so characteristic of much hearty laughter? Possibly, because early man was fairly uninhibited about expressing his pleasurable states, so that this lack of inhibition was also at a highly selective advantage, and thus became an indissoluble and characteristic part of the function of laughter.

And now, to wind all this up, there remains but one matter with which we must deal. It is the relation of the smile to laughter, insofar as it bears upon our theory of the origin of laughter.

Infants begin to laugh at about 12 weeks; they will sometimes smile as early as 6 days. The smile is obviously the precursor of the laugh. A 12-week-old infant will laugh because he is a comparatively sophisticated creature compared to the neonate (first two weeks of postnatal life). This suggests that the older infant laughs not because he is physiologically better able to do so than the neonate, but because he is psychologically rather better equipped to do so. The older infant laughs because he understands: the neonate does not laugh because he is not yet capable of understanding. The smile is to the laugh as the dawn is to the noon's glorious sun. Even though he is himself unable to speak, it is with the infant's beginning understanding of the general meaning of some uttered human sounds that he begins to laugh. Hence, the connection of the origin of laughter with the origins of speech would appear to be indicated by the gradual development of these two capacities in the human infant.

The Myth of Man's Ferocious Nature

The shift in meaning, during the nineteenth century, from the eighteenth-century conception of nature as harmony and design to nature as struggle brought about the eclipse of the concept of harmony as an ideal of human relations, and saw the emergence of the idea that what is just is determined by the arbitrament of force, the survival of the fittest.

Traditional conceptions concerning the innate depravity of man's nature, and the transformation, during the nineteenth century, of this doctrinal teaching into a bulwark of the Darwinian theory of evolution, have led to the belief in our own time that since man's ancestors were "wild animals" resembling the gorilla and chimpanzee, early man must have partaken to a great degree of this wildness. "The wild," "the jungle," "prehistoric man," "Neanderthal man," "the savage," and similar pejoratively used terms have served to condition the thinking of educated people and others for the last hundred years. To behave like a "Neanderthal" meant to behave like a "brute." And the "savage," of course, was very savage, indeed, preserving in his "savage" behavior something of the character of "prehistoric man." Learned scientists were quite as much affected by the traditional and tough Darwinian points of view as was the layman. Hence, when Neanderthal man's skeleton was found, it was reconstructed not in accordance with the anatomical functional traits it exhibited, but in accordance with its reconstructor's, Professor Marcellin Boule's, conception of what such a prehistoric man *ought* to look like! And so, for several generations, the world has had foisted upon it a creature called

"Neanderthal man," characterized by a bestial face, a bull neck, knock-knees, and a stooping gait, usually holding a club in one hand and dragging a female by her hair with the other. This travesty of the facts met with ready acceptance since it was congenial to the intellectual temper of the times, even as it is to ours. Because they are so emotionally satisfying, such ideas will not soon be replaced by the facts. Man is a mythmaking animal who prefers to embrace the myths that keep him comfortable rather than inquire into the facts that enjoin him to think.[45]

If some scientists, who should have known better, served to keep such myths alive, what may be said of the numinous-luminous school of popular-science writers? One thing that can certainly be said of them is that they faithfully reflect the ideas of their time. Indeed, it is in the works of such contemporary writers that we are most likely to find the orthodox beliefs faithfully reproduced. A typical example of such a work is entitled *Prehistoric Man,* by Charles Knight.[46] This work is representative of views concerning prehistoric man that are widely held at the present time. Mr. Knight, who for many years was the distinguished artist at the American Museum of Natural History, takes a Hobbesian view of prehistoric man. For him the life of early man was poor, nasty, brutish, and short. Every man's hand was set against every other man's, and all the creatures of the earth seemed to have lived in a perpetual state of strife or warfare. This is not altogether surprising, since Darwin's favorite phrase in this connection was "the warfare of nature." According to Mr. Knight, "one never knew on retiring whether one would actually be there when morning broke." "The facts show now that a bitter struggle for supremacy has been going on ever since our old world was created." "Man had constructive ideas. He *wanted* things, and if his neighbors had a specially comfortable shelter in which to hide at night, envious thoughts arose and at times he was able to drive them out of the coveted retreat and occupy it himself." "How easy it was to sneak up on an enemy in a neighboring clan and in the dense jungle and tap him none too gently on his thick skull with a heavy club or a piece of sharp stone!" "We have no doubt that it often became a question of who was who in the jungle retreats, and that fierce battles were the result of any chance meetings between our unsavoury antecedents when tribal or family differences were involved." And so on throughout this bloodthirsty book about the purely mythical "fiery little brutes" who have been conjured, not so much out of the pigments of Mr. Knight's imagination, as out of the orthodox viewpoint on these matters, which Mr. Knight has simply rendered more colorful.

Among the purposes served by myths is the justification of the ways of man or of a particular variety of man to other varieties of the kingdom of animated nature. In the same manner myths idealize certain forms of social conditions and justify their maintenance. The myth of "bestial" prehistoric man is of the same nature as the myth of the "savage" or the myth of the "beast," or "the gorilla." Are any of these creatures what we have been led to believe they are by countless "mythologists" masquerading as "authorities," and perpetrating their various ignorances upon an only too willing audience? The answer is that they are not. The "savage" is not savage, the "beast" is not a beast, and the "gorilla" is not, as Mr. Knight and others would have us believe, of "a very cantankerous and irascible disposition, which is part of his ferocious make-up." The very contradictory of all these statements is the truth. "Savages" live cooperatively with one another, and, with few exceptions, seldom bother anyone. Men behave like "beasts" in highly civilized societies, but the beasts of the field do not. As for the gorilla, far from being "very cantankerous and irascible" and "ferocious," it is a very quiet, amiable, and unquarrelsome creature, as innumerable authorities who have observed it both at first hand in its native habitat and under captive conditions have testified. Gorillas have never been observed fighting with one another nor have chimpanzees or orang-utans [47]

The belief in prehistoric man's ferocious nature is so deeply ingrained in our culture, that whenever any findings are presented that could possibly be interpreted as supporting the orthodox credo, it is almost invariably so interpreted. For example, in his fascinating book, *Adventures with the Missing Link*, published in 1959, Professor Raymond Dart[48] has a chapter entitled "The Antiquity of Murder." This is a promising beginning. In this chapter Dart draws attention to the fact that an adolescent jaw of *Australopithecus prometheus*, found at Makapansgat, had been split on both sides and all the front teeth "knocked out." "This dramatic specimen," he writes, "instantly prompted me to study the murderous and apparently cannibalistic manner of life of these violent creatures."

But is the assumption that this adolescent australopithecine was murdered necessary? Could not the blow, if it was delivered by another australopithecine, have been accidental? The question has never been asked. It did not have to be, for if the answer to a question is already known, it is scarcely necessary to ask it. Even professors are not immune from reasoning from unwarranted assumptions to foregone conclusions. Why think of so lackluster an explanation as an "accident" when the more dramatic "murder" is so much more in keeping with the orthodox manner of dealing with these matters? But then there are "the casts of the insides of several man-ape skulls found at Sterkfontein (which) shows that they too had been shattered shortly before death by skull-smashing shocks." Some skulls had had the bones broken from within outward, and this suggests that the brains may have been eaten. This is accompanied by an illustration showing "Australopithecines fighting with bone club and dagger."

Let it be supposed for a moment that Dart's *anatomical* interpretations of the skull fractures are correct; does this necessarily imply that his interpretation of the causes of those fractures is also correct? It does not, for the damage may have been produced in a variety of different ways. But let it further be supposed that the damage was deliberately produced by other australopithecines, and that they ate the brains, and possibly even other parts of other australopithecines; does this, then, necessarily mean that the australopithecines were habitual murderers and cannibals? It does not, any more than it means that any group of men are habitual murderers and cannibals when as a result of famine and starvation they resort to murder and cannibalism. It has happened in our own time among the most civilized of people, and it will happen again. Does this prove that man is murderous and cannibalistic by nature? It does not. Ritual cannibalism is another possible explanation.

It is highly probable that on occasion, as men at similar times have done, australopithecines may have resorted to murder and cannibalism when famine and starvation drove them to it, but even the evidence of Dart's own findings, and the numerous australopithecine finds made elsewhere in Africa, indicate that, if it occurred at all, this was the exceptional rather than the usual form of behavior. The australopithecines, like most other prehistoric men, have become victims of the myth of the "beast." Too many have been too easily deceived by it.

Yet another addition to the myth of the "beast" has been produced from Olduvai. The left parietal or dome bone of the 11- or 12-year-old child found at the oldest site at Olduvai showed a break at the point of impact with radiating fractures. It need scarcely be added that this has been interpreted by its discoverer, Dr. L. S. B. Leakey, as constituting evidence that the child had been murdered. "I think it reasonable to say," writes Dr. Leakey in the October 1961 issue of the *National Geographic,* "that the child received—and probably died from—what in modern police parlance is known as 'a blow from a blunt instrument.'" The "modern police parlance" is an elegant touch; it provides just the "right" decor. The truth is, of course, that one cannot say what that fractured right parietal was due to, but it does lend a dramatic element to the story to introduce the "murder" motif once more, and since that motif fits the book perfectly, the explanation is readily accepted.

In April 1965 Dr. Leakey claimed that three distinct species of man overlapped in time and were living within a range of 100 miles of each other in East Africa, namely, *Zinjanthropus, Homo habilis,* and the pithecanthropine "Chellean" man (or the LLK skull, as Leakey prefers to call it from the site at which it was found). These three "species" of man were, according to Dr. Leakey, in competition with one another. "The time has come," he said at a symposium on the origin of man held at the University of Chicago, "to get away from the 1, 2, 3, 4 idea of man's development. Man developed just like the animals did, with various species living side by side until the weaker died out or were annihilated, leaving the stronger until eventually modern man emerged" (*Science News Letter,* 17 April 1965, p. 243).

Altogether apart from the doubtful validity of the claim for these forms as three different species, the suggestion that the competition was of a combative kind, with the weaker succumbing to the stronger, is based on nothing more than the nineteenth-century stereotyped manner of thinking about competition. There is no evidence whatever for such competition. It requires to be pointed out that cooperation is also a form of competition, and that as such it undoubtedly played a highly significant role in the evolution of man. What is most likely is that, if the members of these three different groups ever met, they did what peoples have always done: they interbred, and by such hybridization formed a common gene pool, resulting in descendants somewhat different from the original hybridizing forms. Although we observe the results of it virtually every day among us, there is a marked tendency to shy away from any consideration of hybridization as an important factor in the evolution of man. Possibly this evasive behavior has some connection with the fact that hybridization, "race mixture," has quite unjustifiably been given a bad name. Certainly there are many among us who prefer to think of man's evolution as unsullied by "mongrelization." But this is a modern prejudice. It suits the book of such thinkers to believe that the "higher" forms exterminated the "lower" forms, so that by a series of such progressive exterminations the "higher" forms gradually replaced the "lower." It is such thinking that gave rise to the belief, still prevalent among some anthropologists, that Neanderthal man, instead of contributing to the evolution of modern man through the usual processes of evolution, including hybridization, was in fact exterminated by him. There is no more evidence for this extermination theory than there is for it in the case of Leakey's East African forms. When the final story of man's evolution comes to be written, it will probably be seen to have been, among other things, a history of increasing migrations and "mongrelizations." All of us are mongrels, and we are all the better for being so.

It is a prejudice, inherited from earlier generations of thinkers, influenced by the combative "survival of the fittest" schools of thought, that "higher" forms replaced "lower" forms of man by extermination. It is at the present time quite impossible to speak with certainty upon the subject, but it seems highly improbable that extermination played any role whatever in the evolution of man, and that hybridization and cooperation played a highly significant role in that evolution.

The latest contribution to the doctrine of man's innate depravity, as the Victorians so charmingly called it, is a highly sophisticated work written by the playwright Robert Ardrey. This work, published in 1961, is significantly entitled *African Genesis: A Personal Investigation into the Animal Origins and Nature of Man*.[49] The first part of the book is devoted to a demonstration, which the author brings off quite convincingly, of the validity of Professor Raymond Dart's claims for an osteodontokeratic culture among the australopithecines. But in the second part of the book Mr. Ardrey makes one of the most remarkable extrapolations from the first part I have ever read in any work. Mr. Ardrey argues that since the australopithecines made and used tools, and employed some of them as implements with which to bash in the skulls of baboons, the australopithecines were therefore "killers," and that *therefore* human beings are "killers" by nature! Mr. Ardrey's book constitutes, perhaps, the most illuminating example of the manner in which a man's prejudices may get in the way of his reason and distort his view of the evidence. Mr. Ardrey refers to some of his early personal experiences of violence which convinced him of the murderousness of human nature. Hence, when through the distorting glass of his prejudgments he looks at a tool it becomes not simply a scraper but a weapon, a knife becomes a dagger, and even a large canine tooth becomes "the natural dagger that is the hallmark of all hunting mammals," while in "the armed hunting primate" it becomes "a redundant instrument." "With the advent of the lethal weapon natural selection turned from the armament of the jaw to the armament of the hand."

But the teeth are no more an armament than is the hand, and it is entirely to beg the question to call them so. Virtually all the members of the order of primates, other than man, have large canine teeth, and these animals, with the exception of the baboons, are predominantly vegetarians, and it is because they are vegetarians that they require large canine teeth; that such teeth may, on occasion, serve a protective purpose is entirely secondary to their main function, which is to rip and shred the hard outer coverings of plant foods. Primates are not usually belligerent unless provoked, and the more carefully they are observed the more remarkably revealing do their unquarrelsomeness and cooperativeness become. The myth of the ferocity of "wild animals" constitutes one of Western man's supreme rationalizations, for it not only has served to "explain" to him the origins of his own aggressiveness, but also to relieve him of the responsibility for it—for since it is "innate," derived from his early apelike ancestors, he can hardly, so he rationalizes, be blamed for it! And some have gone so far as to add that nothing can be done about it, and that therefore wars and juvenile delinquents, as Mr. Ardrey among others tell us, will always be with us! From one not-so-minor error to another Mr. Ardrey sweeps on to the grand fallacy.

At this point it needs to be said that Mr. Ardrey's views are firmly based on and derived from those of Professor Raymond Dart, who in an article entitled, "The Predatory Transition from Ape to Man,"[50] published in 1953, argued that man's animal ancestry was carnivorous, predatory, and cannibalistic in origin, and went on to add that "The blood-bespattered, slaughter-gutted archives of human history from the earliest Egyptian and Sumerian records to the most recent atrocities of the Second World War accord with early universal cannibalism, with animal and human sacrificial practices or their substitutes in formalized religions and with the worldwide scalping, head-hunting, body-mutilating and necrophiliac practices of mankind in proclaiming this common bloodlust differentiator, this predaceous habit, this mark of Cain that separates man dietetically from his anthropoidal relatives and allies him rather with the deadliest of Carnivora."[51]

Mr. Ardrey puts this in the following words: "The human being in the most fundamental aspects of his soul and body is nature's last if temporary word on the subject of the armed predator. And human history must be read in these terms."

In furtherance of this argument "tools" for Mr. Ardrey are not only identified as "weapons," but, he goes on to imply, nay, indeed, he states, "that when any scientist writes the word, 'tool,' as a rule he refers to weapons. This is a euphemism" (p. 306).

Perhaps this opportunity should be taken to assure Mr. Ardrey that when scientists write the word "tool" they mean exactly what they say, and that euphemisms are not, as Mr. Ardrey says, "normal to all natural science" (p. 306). Some tools may be used as weapons and even manufactured as such, but most tools of prehistoric man, from his earliest days, were most certainly not designed primarily to serve as weapons. Knives were designed to cut, scrapers to scrape, choppers to chop, and hammers to hammer. That such tools could be used as weapons is true, but to serve as weapons was not their primary purpose nor the reason for which they were devised.

"Man," Mr. Ardrey tells us, "is a predator whose natural instinct is to kill with a weapon" (p. 316). But man has no instincts, and if he had, they could hardly include the use of weapons in their psychophysical structure.

Early man's hunting, according to Mr. Ardrey, was due to instinctive belligerence, not to the hunger for food. "When the necessities of the hunting life encountered the basic primate instincts, then all were intensified. Conflicts became lethal, territorial arguments minor wars. . . . The creature who had once killed only through circumstance now killed for a living" (p. 317). This was "the aggressive imperative."

The evidence does not support Mr. Ardrey's theories. Whatever "the basic primate instincts" may be, they are not what Mr. Ardrey implies. Indeed, when he forgets himself, he writes of "the non-aggressive, vegetarian primate," which is precisely what all primates tend to be. But Mr. Ardrey would have us believe the contrary: the basic primate instincts according to him are aggressive. And, of course, with the assumption of hunting as a way of life, these, according to him, would become intensified. But in previous pages, and at greater length elsewhere, I have given the evidence for the contrary view. This evidence renders Mr. Ardrey's interpretations quite unacceptable. Everything points to the nonviolence of the greater part of early man's life, to the contribution made by the increasing development of cooperative activities, the very social process of hunting itself, the invention of speech, the development of food-getting and food-preparing tools, and the like. These facts are never once mentioned by Mr. Ardrey, except perhaps obliquely as a doctrine which scheming scientists have foisted upon an unsuspecting world. The truth is that Mr. Ardrey is arguing a thesis. It is the thesis of "innate depravity." It is an unsound thesis, and it is a dangerous one, because it perpetuates unsound views which justify, and even tend to sanction, the violence which man is capable of learning, but which Mr. Ardrey erroneously believes to be inherited from man's australopithecine ancestors.

When man hunts he is the predator and the hunted animal is the prey. But prehistoric man did not hunt for pleasure, in order to satisfy his "predatory instincts." He hunted for food, to satisfy his hunger, and the hunger of those who were dependent upon him. He did not hunt because he was a "killer," any more than contemporary men are "killers" who kill animals in abattoirs so that others may eat them. Prehistoric man was no more a "killer" than we are "killers" when we sit down at table to consume a chicken or a steak which, by proxy, someone else has "killed" for us. It would be interesting to know who are the "murderers," the men who are paid to slaughter the animals we eat, or we who pay the cashier at the supermarket? Or perhaps it is really the owner of the store in which we buy meat who is the "murderer," the "killer"? Prehistoric man hunted because he desired to live—*that* hardly makes him a killer, any more than our continuing in the habit of eating meat makes us killers.

When Mr. Ardrey admiringly presents us with *West Side Story* as a "vivid portrait of natural man," in which "we watch our animal legacy unfold its awful power," in the form of juvenile delinquents in their "timeless struggle over territory, as lunatic in the New York streets as it is logical in our animal heritage," we can only say, "in police parlance," that it is worthy of William Golding's *Lord of the Flies,* in which a similar view of the depravity of human nature is unfolded. In Golding's novel two groups of children, abandoned on an island, take to hunting each other to the death. This novel has a wide readership on American college campuses, and it has recently been made into a film. Its appeal to young people is not strange, for in the world of violence in which they live Golding's novel supplies them with an easy "explanation." I understand that the novel is used in some sociology courses as a good illustration of "innate depravity," of the alleged natural nastiness of man. It could hardly be expected to be otherwise.[52]

Mr. Ardrey has further elaborated his views in a book entitled *The Territorial Imperative,*[53] published in August 1966. In this work Mr. Ardrey endeavors to show that man's aggressiveness is based on his allegedly innate territorial nature. Man, he argues, has an innate compulsion to gain and defend exclusive territory, preserve or property. The territorial nature of man, he says, is genetic and ineradicable.

Mr. Ardrey devotes the greater part of his book to a discussion of territoriality in many different kinds of animals. He attempts to show that territoriality in animals is innately determined. The informed student of these matters would be interested in knowing why the evidence has not been considered which leads to the opposite conclusion. Mr. Ardrey writes that "The disposition to possess a territory is innate. . . . But its position and borders will be learned" (p. 25). Certainly it is biologically and socially valuable for many animals to possess their own special territory, and certainly there are strong drives in most animals to defend their territory against trespassers, but such drives are not necessarily innate. They may be learned in just the same way in which animals learn the position and borders of their territory. Territory is defined as an area defended by its occupant against competing members of the same species. But there are many animals that do not exhibit such behavior. The California ground squirrel, adult male long-tailed field mice, she-wolves, the red fox, the Iowan prairie spotted skunk, the northern plains red fox, and in the superfamily to which man belongs, the Hominoidea, the orang-utan, the chimpanzee, and the gorilla, as well as many other animals. As Bourlière has observed in his admirable book, *The Natural History of Animals,* "It would seem that territorial behavior is far from being as important in mammals as in birds."[54] Somehow, Ardrey manages to neglect to consider the significance of these many exceptional cases. And while he does mention the chimpanzee, he omits any reference to the orang-utan[55] and the gorilla.[56] On the naturally amiable chimpanzee's non-territoriality he comments, "The chimpanzee has demonstrated, I presume, that we must reckon on some degree of innate amity in the primate potential; but as I have indicated, it is a very small candle on a very dark night" (p. 222).

On the contrary, the non-territoriality of great apes constitutes, one would have thought, a very bright beacon in a cloudless sky, for if, as is evident, man's nearest collateral relatives are wanting in anything resembling an inborn territorial drive, it is highly improbable that any form of man was ever characterized by such a drive. Arguments based on fish, birds, and other animals are strictly for them. They have no relevance for man. "The otherwise admirable animal," the chimpanzee, is for Mr. Ardrey, "an evolutionary failure" (p. 223), while the aggressive baboon is "an outrageous evolutionary success" (p. 222).

Apparently evolutionary failure or success is to be measured by the yardstick of population number. The baboons are many, the great apes are few and are threatened with extinction. There is little evidence that the great apes were ever numerous, but that they are today few in number and threatened with extinction is all too tragically true. The diminishing numbers of these animals is due not to their lack of territoriality, but to the encroachments upon both their habitats and their lives by men with weapons against which they are utterly defenseless. No matter how highly developed their territorial sense might have been, they could never have withstood these onslaughts.

What we are witnessing in Mr. Ardrey's "territorial imperative" is a revival in modern dress of the good old "Instinct of Property" which, together with such oddities as the "Instinct of Philoprogenitiveness" and other such curiosities were repudiated by scientists half a century ago.[57] It is all very old hat, and as John Ray, the seventeenth-century English naturalist put it, "Let him make use of instinct who cannot make use of reason."[58]

Mr. Ardrey deplores the rejection of "instinct" in man, and actually goes so far as to suggest that "a party line" has appeared in American science designed to perpetuate the "falsehood" that instincts do not exist in man. Mr. Ardrey needs the concept of "open instincts," of innate factors, to support his theorizing. But that requirement constitutes the fatal flaw in his theory, the rift in the playwright's lute, for man is man because he has no instincts, because everything he is and has become he has learned, acquired, from his culture, from the man-made part of the environment, from other human beings. Mr. Ardrey declines to accept that fact, being more enamored of his theories than he is of facts. This is rather a pity because he would serve himself and us all a great deal more worthily if he would only realize that a scientist is not interested in proving or in disproving theories, in believing or in disbelieving, but in discovering what *is*. Thomas Henry Huxley once remarked of Herbert Spencer that his idea of a tragedy was a beautiful theory killed by an ugly fact. In Mr. Ardrey's case the beautiful facts render his ugly theories otiose.

What is the explanation of the appeal such books have for so many people? Golding's novel is a rattling good story. Ardrey's books are excitingly written and hold the reader spellbound. But these qualities are not the secret of their appeal. What, then, is?

Such books are both congenial to the temper of the times and comforting to the reader who is seeking some sort of absolution for his sins. It is gratifying to find father confessors who will relieve one of the burdensome load of guilt we bear by shifting the responsibility for it to our "natural inheritance," our "innate aggressiveness."

If it is our "nature" to be what we are, if we are the lineal descendants of our "murderous" ancestors, we can hardly be blamed or blame ourselves for the sin of being little more than made-over apes. Our orneriness is explained, and so is the peccant behavior of children, juvenile delinquency, crime, rape, murder, arson, and war, not to mention every other form of violence. It is all simply explained: it is due to man's innate aggressiveness.

There is nothing new in all this. We have heard it before. During the latter half of the 19th century, and during the early part of the 20th century, this viewpoint formed the foundation for the doctrine of "Social Darwinism." It was implied in such ideas as "The Survival of the Fittest" and "The Struggle for Existence," and in such phrases as "The weakest go to the wall," "Competition is the life-blood of a nation," and the like.

Such ideas were not merely taken to explain, but were actually used to justify, violence and war. As General von Bernhardi put it in 1912, "War is a biological necessity . . . it is as necessary as the struggle of the elements in Nature . . . it gives a biologically just decision, since its decisions rest on the very nature of things."[59] One wonders what von Bernhardi would have said after the "biologically just" defeat of Germany in two World Wars? No doubt, the general would have had little difficulty in finding an "explanation."

The new liturgy of "innate aggression," as an explanation of man's proclivities to violent behavior, does not seek to justify that behavior, but by thus "explaining" it to point the direction in which we must proceed if we are to exercise some measure of control over it. Toward this end, Dr. Konrad Lorenz, one of the founders of the modern science of ethology —the study of behavior under natural conditions of life—has dedicated himself in his latest book, *On Aggression*, published in April 1966.[60]

In *On Aggression* Lorenz has set out his views at length. In many respects they parallel those of Ardrey.

Ardrey's and Lorenz's views suffer from the same fatal defect, namely, extrapolation from other animals to man.

Why do reasonable beings behave so unreasonably, asks Lorenz. And he answers, "Undeniably, there must be superlatively strong factors which are able to overcome the commands of individual reason so completely and which are so obviously impervious to experience and learning" (p. 237). "All these amazing paradoxes, however, find an unconstrained explanation, falling into place like the pieces of a jigsaw puzzle, if one assumes that human behavior, far from being determined by reason and cultural tradition alone, is still subject to all the laws prevailing in all phylogenetically adapted instinctive behavior. Of these laws we possess a fair amount of knowledge from studying the instincts of animals" (p. 237).

It is in these sentences that the flaws in Lorenz's argument are exhibited. First he assumes that man's frequent irrational behavior is phylogenetically based. Second, this enables him to conclude that the "laws" derived from the "study of the instincts of animals" are applicable to man.

There is, in fact, not the slightest evidence or ground for assuming that the phylogenetically adapted instinctive behavior of other animals is in any way relevant to the discussion of the motive-forces of human behavior. The fact is, that with the exception of the instinctoid reactions in infants to sudden withdrawals of support and to sudden loud noises, the human being is entirely instinctless.

Those who speak of "innate aggression" in man appear to be lacking in any understanding of the uniqueness of man's evolutionary history. Unacquainted with the facts or else undeterred by them they insist on fitting whatever facts they are acquainted with into their theories. In so doing they commit the most awful excesses. But, as is well known, nothing succeeds like excess. Lorenz's assumptions and interpretations are typical.

"There is evidence" he writes, "that the first inventors of pebble tools—the African Australopithecines—promptly used their new weapon to kill not only game, but fellow members of their species as well" (p. 239). We have already dealt with this "evidence" on an earlier page, and found it wanting.

Lorenz continues, "Peking Man, the Prometheus who learned to preserve fire, used it to roast his brothers: beside the first traces of the regular use of fire lie the mutilated and roasted bones of Sinanthropus pekinesis himself" (p. 239).

Lorenz's interpretation of the "evidence" is one he shares with many others, but it is gravely doubted whether it is sound. The cracked bones of Peking man may represent the remains of individuals who died during a famine and who may well have been eaten by their surviving associates. This sort of thing has been known to occur among most peoples of whom we have any knowledge. There is, however, no record of any people, prehistoric, nonliterate, or anywhere in the annals of human history, who made a habit of killing their fellow men in order to dine off them. It is absurd to suggest that Peking man used fire "to roast his brothers." Does Lorenz seriously believe that Peking man made a practice of "roast brother"? Has it never occurred to Lorenz that, like some contemporary peoples, burning the corpse may have been Peking man's way of disposing of the dead?

Lorenz writes, "One shudders at the thought of a creature as irascible as all pre-human primates are, swinging a well-sharpened hand-ax" (pp. 241–242). For a serious student of animal behavior Dr. Lorenz appears to be singularly ill-informed on the temperaments of prehuman primates. It is not "irascibility" which is the term most frequently used to describe the temperaments of "pre-human primates" by those who know them best, but "amiability." The field studies of Schaller on the gorilla, of Goodall on the chimpanzee, of Harrisson on the orang-utan, as well as those of others,[6] show these creatures to be anything but irascible, and there is not the least reason to believe that man's pre-human primate ancestors were any different. Captured monkeys or apes and monkeys in zoos are not the best examples from which to deduce the behavior of such creatures under natural conditions.

Lorenz writes of early man faced with "the counter-pressures of hostile and neighboring hordes" (p. 243). Again, there exists not the slightest evidence of hostility between neighboring hordes of early man. The populations of early man were very small, a few score or a few hundred individuals at most. "Neighboring hordes" would have been few and far between, and when they met it is extremely unlikely that they would have been any less friendly than food-gathering hunting peoples are today.

"The hostile neighboring tribe," writes Lorenz, "once the target at which to discharge phylogenetically programmed aggression, has now withdrawn to an ideal distance, hidden behind a curtain, if possible of iron. Among the many phylogenetically adopted norms of human social behavior, there is hardly one that does not need to be controlled and kept on a leash by responsible morality" (p. 253).

And there we have it: man's aggressiveness is "phylogenetically programmed," and can be kept within bounds only by moral controls. It has never occurred to Lorenz, who knows a great deal about greylag goslings, but apparently very little else that is not in the realm of 19th century speculative desk-anthropology, that far from being innate, man's aggressiveness is a learned form of behavior. There is absolutely no evidence—indeed, the evidence is entirely in the opposite direction—that man is in any way "programmed" to behave aggressively.

Throughout the two million years of man's evolution the highest premium has been placed on cooperation, not merely *intra*group cooperation, but also upon *inter*group cooperation, or else there would be no human beings today.[62] Intra- or intergroup hostilities, in small populations, would have endangered the very existence of such populations, for any serious reduction in numbers would have made the maintenance of such populations impossible. There is not the slightest evidence nor is there the least reason to suppose that such conflicts ever occurred in human populations before the development of agricultural-pastoral communities, not much more than 10,000 years ago.

The myth of early man's aggressiveness belongs in the

same class as the myth of "the beast," that is, the belief that most if not all "wild" animals are ferocious killers. In the same class belongs the myth of "the jungle," "the wild," "the warfare of Nature," and, of course, the myth of "innate depravity" or "original sin." These myths represent the projection of our *acquired* deplorabilities upon the screen of "Nature." What we are unwilling to acknowledge as essentially of our own making, the consequence of our own disordering in the man-made environment, we saddle upon "Nature," upon "phylogenetically programmed" or "innate" factors. It is very comforting, and if, somehow, one can connect it all with findings on greylag goslings, studied for their "releaser mechanisms," and relate the findings on fish, birds, and other animals to man, it makes everything all the easier to understand and to accept.

What, in fact, such writers do, in addition to perpetrating their wholly erroneous interpretation of human nature, is to divert attention from the real sources of man's aggression and destructiveness, namely, the many false and contradictory values by which, in an overcrowded, highly competitive, threatening world, he so inoperatively attempts to live. It is not man's nature, but his nurture, in such a world, that requires our attention.

The evidence as we are able to judge it, on the basis of field observations among living primates, indicates the deep-seated nature of the cooperative drives which bind the members of primate societies together and preserve them. Among early men these cooperative drives were undoubtedly intensified for the very reason that every member of early human society was in an even more interdependent relation to his fellows than the members of any other primate group had ever been. The critical state of immaturity in which the human infant is born, and the long period of dependency which is characteristic of him, have from the first intensified and reinforced the cooperative organization of the responses from others upon which the human child is dependent for his survival and his development as a human being.[63]

The human family is the basic cooperative organization. As Professor Hugh Miller has said in his important book *Progress and Decline* (Los Angeles, 1963), human character, what we call "personality," "is given its impulsion and direction not by sexual passion," nor yet by conflict, "but by conjugal devotion, filial piety, and parental love. Not by nine months of pregnancy, but by a dozen or score years of upbringing is man gestated."[64] Upon these traits, in reciprocal interaction with each other, have the very foundations of every human society from the earliest days rested. Cooperation, *not* conflict, was evidently the selectively most valuable form of behavior for man taken at any stage of his evolutionary history, and, surely, quite as evidently never more so than today. Indeed, so it has always been. Human society especially, if it is anything, is a cooperation; it is essentially the experience, the means that fits human beings not to their external environment so much as to one another. It must never be forgotten that society is fundamentally, essentially, and in all ways a cooperative enterprise, an enterprise designed to keep men in touch with one another. Without the cooperation of its members society cannot survive, and the society of man has survived because the cooperativeness of its members made survival possible—it was not an adventitious individual here and there who did so, but the group. In human societies the individuals who are most likely to survive are those who are best enabled to do so by their group. As Miller says, effective selection is of whatever secures group-persistence. The effective environment of the group is that provided by the group itself, the cultural environment, and it is in this that the young must be nurtured. Man learns to respond not directly to the physical environment, but indirectly through the cultural means which he has been taught by his culture. It is culture that fits human beings to meet the challenges of their environment, not genetically determined instinct, but genetically based, learned ability, intelligence. It is through the cultural process, which is of its very essence cooperative, that the growing member of the group learns what his culture expects of him and what he may reciprocally expect from it. Every culture aims to make each of its members a cooperative member of the group.

The group buffers the individual against the environmental pressures which, as an individual, he could not meet alone. This is, of course, most evident during the long extended dependency of the human child. By being nurtured, cooperated with by others, he learns to nurture and to cooperate with others. And, indeed, all his basic drives are oriented in that direction. It is these drives or needs that are drawn upon in every society as providing the conditions of growth for the new generation.

It would have been a selective disadvantage for a creature designed to have been as devoted to violence as some have

tried to make out that man is, to have burdened itself with
the care of the young for as long as man must, and furthermore to have jeopardized its continuation in "the struggle
for existence" by limiting itself to one offspring at a birth.
Man, on the contrary, has retained the anthropoidal monotocous birth (one at a birth) because the smaller the number of offspring the more effectively they can be protected
from the pressures of the external environment, and the more
efficiently each can be nurtured and culturalized.

Individual and Group

When man's ancestors found themselves on the savannas, it
was not as the result of a sudden cataclysm, but as a consequence of a gradual and long process extended over many
millennia. Man's ancestors were not precipitately expelled
from a Garden of Eden into the inhospitable savanna, where
the dry winds and the sirocco blow, creatures, as Wordsworth
put it, with:

> Blank misgivings . . .
> Moving about in worlds not realized.

The forests withered slowly, and their replacement by savannas was very gradual. It is necessary to emphasize these
points because the suggestion has been made that since the
savannas were hazardous, "to deal with tooth-and-claw times,
organization of some sort was essential. . . . Individualists had
to bow to a social order rigid enough to insure survival. Thus
a freewheeling species was moulded into a close-knit way of
life, learned to submerge individuality, and form deep and
intense emotional attachments to the organized group. . . .
The forest ape, evidently, had evolved into a creature so intelligent and so individualistic that he could not adapt to
open-savanna dangers without developing a permanent source
of tension." Conflict between the individual and the group,
so runs this theory, could not be resolved. "So gradually our
ancestors learned to live with their tensions. And today the
development of man as a species may actually depend on the
existence of conflict. In other words, what was once an ob-
stacle has become an essential element in our evolution, a
built-in source of discontent which drives us on." And this
discontent, Mr. Pfeiffer points out, has been, and continues
to be, the mother of progress.[65]

It is an interesting theory, but it will not withstand critical examination. When contemporary apes are observed to come out of the forests into the savannas, they often appear to be jittery—but so do other animals. Indeed, as Hediger has pointed out, most mammals tend to be chronically slightly jittery, whereas man differs from them in not being so.[66] In any event, the theory which Mr. Pfeiffer so ably expounds is based on the utterly erroneous "tooth-and-claw" notion. The principal hazard, virtually the only hazard, that early man had to face, and man has had to face throughout his history, was not the danger of the unprovoked attacks of other animals, but the hazard of an insufficient food supply. This might result in some anxiety, but not in the kind of jitteriness and tension that Mr. Pfeiffer suggests. It is a fact that every breath a human being takes is preceded by a faint phobic stir.[67] Man *is* an anxious creature, for a certain amount of anxiety is a very necessary trait if so precariously poised a creature is to survive in the environments in which he finds himself. But man's anxieties have nothing to do with the conditions of his early evolution, but rather with the manner of his birth, the creation of the first anxiety, and the necessity to go on satisfying one's basic needs.[68] Early man with his intelligence had little to fear from other animals except when there were any so misguided as to seek to make a meal of him. It is known to most knowledgeable observers that virtually all animals who have had experience of man tend to give him a wide berth. He is far too formidable an adversary with his large body size and dangerous weapons. In man's search for food jitteriness would have been a handicap. What one needs is an uncluttered mind, clear and bent to the single purpose of securing the vital element, food. Far from the individual's interest being in opposition to that of the group, all the evidence indicates that his own welfare has always been best served when it has been devoted to the interest not of self but of the group, and this is especially true at the hunting level. Drives of this directiveness appear to be built into the biological structure of man, and these are quite incompatible with the existence of those individualistic tendencies of which Mr. Pfeiffer speaks.

Man is a restless, searching creature, always living on the verge of something, on the borderlands of something more! It is a trait he shares with many other creatures, and it is one which, because of his unique capacities, he has been able to put creatively to good use. It is not a neurotic tension, but a drive essential to exploration, the satisfaction of curiosity, and the inventiveness and creativeness so eminently characteristic of man. By the very nature of his being man lives in continuously changing situations. He is always on the threshold, entering into one situation from another, emerging from one into another. His situation is intrinsically historical, consisting simultaneously of what it is emerging out of and what it is moving into, an ambiguously dynamic relation between necessity (of what has been and the limits it imposes upon the future) and possibility (of what may or may not yet be).[69] The dynamic relation between necessity and possibility is the link between existence and living, between being and becoming, the activity, the discontent which is the mother of invention.

The significance of man's extended period of immaturity and childhood dependency has already been discussed. We have now to discuss one of the interesting evolutionary mechanisms which is thought to have contributed toward that development.

Neoteny—The Retention of Early Developmental Characteristics

If one has to learn to be a funtioning, intelligent, human being, with learned behavior substituted for instinctually predetermined behavior, an appreciable amount of time must be available during which the trained skills of intelligent behavior may be acquired. The developmental mechanism by means of which this extension of time for learning was achieved appears, in part, to have been through a process which resulted in the retention in the later postnatal developmental stages of the individual of the fetal or juvenile plasticity of ancestral forms. This process by which the young (fetal or juvenile) features of the ancestor are retained in the mature stages of postnatal development is known as *neoteny*—the developmental retention of fetal or juvenile characters in the adult.

The suggestion is, then, that many of the changes which led to the appearance of distinctively human traits were brought about by neoteny, that man, as the Dutch anthropologist Louis Bolk pointed out, had developed as a fetalized form. Man exhibits many characters which resemble those of fetal apes, some of which are listed below.

NEOTENOUS CHARACTERS IN MAN

Retention of cranial flexure
Long neck
Forward position of foramen magnum
Orbits under cranial cavity
Flatness of face (orthognathy)
Retarded closure of cranial sutures
Large volume of brain
Small face and large braincase
Roundheadedness (brachycephaly)
Small teeth
Late eruption of teeth
Absence of brow ridges
Absence of cranial crests
Thinness of skull bones
Globular form of skull
Relative hairlessness of body
Lack of pigment in some groups
Thin nails
Nonrotation of big toe
Low birth weight
External gestation
Prolonged dependency period
Prolonged growth period

In the fetus of all mammals and most vertebrates the axis of the head forms a right angle with that of the trunk, the cranial flexure. In all mammals, with the exception of man, a rotation of the head occurs during the later stages of development so that the head assumes an orientation that is continuous with the direction of the backbone, as, for example, in the adult dog (Fig. 25). Man, on the other hand, retains the cranial flexure, his face oriented in a plane at right angles to the axis of his body. The visual axis, the line of sight, of both dog and man is horizontal; the dog's body is also horizontal while that of man is vertical. In the adult great apes the position of the body is in between, in conformity with the habitual obliquely quadrupedal form of locomotion, and the axis of the head is also intermediate, the foramen magnum (through which the spinal cord at the base of the skull passes) being situated more posteriorly than it is in either the fetal ape or in man. Thus, whatever it was that brought the erect posture about in the earliest manlike forms was probably

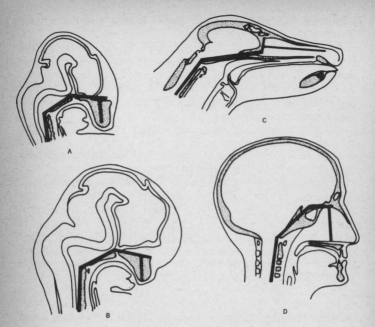

FIG. 25 Midsections through the head showing the angle which the head makes with the trunk in *A:* embryo dog; *B:* embryo man; *C:* adult dog; and *D:* adult man. (*Redrawn from Bolk.*)

genetically facilitated by the retention in postnatal development of a fetal condition which in other mammals is limited only to their intrauterine state of development.

Man's flat-facedness is also a fetal character. It is interesting to speculate that since orthognathy is limited to the early fetal stages of development in apes, the fetal developmental stages at which the neotenous mutations occurred in man's ancestors that led to orthognathy in man must have occurred fairly early —a point to which we shall return.

The sutures of the braincase remain open in man until all growth has been completed, and long after the brain has achieved its maximum growth. While in the apes the cranial sutures begin to close within the first few years of life, in man they do not generally commence to close before the end of the twenty-seventh year. That there should be a close correlation between the duration of the early learning period of man and the growth of the brain is not surprising (see Table V).

Since the brain's growth in volume is completed by the twentieth year, the cranial sutures must remain open at least until this period of growth has been completed. Occasionally, owing to some pathologic cause, the sutures unite in early childhood and prevent the brain from growing, with the result that such children remain mentally retarded all their lives. The major and fundamental part of human learning takes place during the first five years of life, and, as will be seen from Table V, it is during this period that the greater part of brain growth is accomplished.

A point of great significance is that the human brain accelerates in growth and development during the latter stages of fetal life, and continues to grow and develop throughout the first two decades of life. The brain of a three-year-old child, as we have already seen, is almost the size and weight of that of an adult. By the age of six years the brain has generally virtually achieved full adult size. In man the active growth of the brain far exceeds that of any other primate. At birth the mean weight of the brain is about 350 grams (12.5 ounces), or approximately one-fourth of its adult weight. The growth of the brain is very different from that of the rest of the body, being quite explosive during the first year, when it more than doubles to a weight of 825 grams (30 ounces)—a gain of 475 grams (17 ounces). In the second year the gain is almost 275 grams, in the third year about 175 grams, and at the rate of about 70 grams up to the end of the fifth year, when the brain weight reaches 1230 grams (44 ounces). From the sixth to the tenth year the increment varies as follows: 19 grams between five and six years, 8 grams between six and seven years, 46 grams between seven and eight years, and 10 grams between nine and ten years. After the first decade and to the end of the second decade, the increment is less than 3 grams a year—to a total of 1378 grams (49 ounces).

At birth the infant brain is about 25 per cent of its adult size, and by the end of the first year 60 per cent of total brain growth is achieved, and by the end of the third year 85 per cent. In the great apes the greater part of brain growth is achieved within the first year. In the rhesus monkey and in the gibbon 70 per cent of the brain growth has been achieved by birth, and the remainder is completed within the first six months. In the great apes the active period of brain growth occurs during the first eleven months, and in man during the first thirty-six months. Complete growth of the brain in man is not accomplished until the end of the second decade of life. As Keith has pointed out, in this prolongation of cerebral growth and development we see an important, "if not the most important, feature of human evolution—namely, the time taken to assemble and to organize the myriads of nerve cells and of nerve tracts which enter into the structure of man's brain." This process, as Keith adds, is a striking exemplification of the principle of neoteny, and it is a process which assists us to understand something of the manner in which the evolution of that most unique of all traits, the human mind, came about.

The postnatal growth (increase in size) of the human brain maintains the late fetal rate of growth for the first three years. Development (increase in complexity) of the human brain proceeds at a cumulative rate under the influence of the cultural environment, and improves upon the rate of growth and development of the infant ape brain long after the latter has ceased to grow and develop.

The milk teeth of the great apes more closely resemble those of adult man than they do those of adult apes, so that it is not surprising to find, for example, that the milk teeth of the australopithecines resemble more closely the permanent teeth of modern man than they do those of adult australopithecines. In the long delayed eruption of both the milk and the permanent teeth in man we again perceive a neotenous trait, the prolongation of the toothless state of the fetus. In all the other physical traits listed man more closely resembles the fetal ape than he does the adult. The prolonged dependency and growth periods are to be regarded as prolongations of the fetal dependency and growth periods.

One of the consequences of the prolonged dependency of man is that it involves a rather long nursing period, not longer than is the case in apes, but long for so active a species. Therefore, in adaptation to the assumption of the erect posture and the shrinkage of the jaws, there has been a further adaptive response in the form of the development of hemispherical breasts in the female, and the unique response to this in the form of the everted mucous membranous lips of man. Everted lips are much better adapted to suckling at a hemispherical surface than are the thin lips of anthropoids. Just as the cheeks of the baby with their suctorial pads of fat are very different from what they are in the later child or adult, so

does the character of the lips differ in the baby from what
they will later become in the child or adult. The newborn
baby's lips, as we have already observed, are characterized
by a median papilla (which is sometimes mistaken for an
abnormal condition). This papilla, usually on the upper lip,
enables the baby to secure a better hold on the breast.

It is reasonably clear that what is inherited by the organism
has in part been acquired as a consequence of interaction of
the genetic constitution (the genotype) with environment
during development. It is during the process of individual
development that mutations acquire their visible, phenotypic,
expression. Any mutation which serves to produce a relative
retardation of somatic development, so that the descendant
fails to pass through several of the developmental stages of
the ancestor, will result in the descendant's exhibiting a pattern of growth which in the adult stage represents a retention
of the ancestral fetal or youthful pattern. Zoologists know
of many such cases, in which rates of development, the retention of an embryonic or youthful character and its extension in the adult, the duration of developmental periods, and
the termination of development are affected by mutations
which may have distinct and marked effects upon adult form.
Such neotenous mutations may spread rapidly in a small
population, and it is suggested that under such conditions the
fetal or juvenile developmental stage of a pithecanthropine
or similar type could have become very quickly consolidated
in the descendant group. A fetalized pithecanthropine, to
judge from the juvenile Modjokerto skull, or a fetalized
australopithecine, to judge from the juvenile *Australopithecus
africanus,* would more closely resemble modern man than
these fossil juvenile forms would the adult members of their
own type. The milk teeth, for example, of the australopithecines are more like the milk teeth of modern children, but
the permanent teeth are more like those of apes. In almost
all the traits in which the juvenile members of these fossil
forms differ from the living apes and their own adult forms
they most closely resemble modern man, for example, in the
comparatively globular form of the skull, the thinness of the
skull bones, the absence of brow ridges, the absence of crests,
the form of the teeth, and the relative size and form of the
brain. There can be little doubt as to the form and characters
of the fetal forms of the australopithecine and pithecanthropine types—these almost certainly would have more closely
resembled the human than the anthropoid. It is by the reten-

tion of such fetal and juvenile characters in the adult, particularly in the head region, by neoteny, that quite early in the history of the human species the evolution of a neanthropic type of man could have been facilitated.

As long ago as 1923 Keith, in commenting on the ideas of Bolk, remarked that "Man's outstanding structural peculiarities have been produced during the embryonic and fetal stages of his developmental history." In 1925 he wrote, "This intra-uterine period is one which gives every opportunity for the working out of new inventions." And again, in 1947, "It is during the intrauterine phase that nearly all revolutionary changes in structure have been introduced." Professor M. R. Drennan, and more recently, Professor A. A. Abbie, have argued that in the study of man's physical evolution anthropologists have paid insufficient attention to the developing intrauterine organism, that is, to the embryo and fetus, and too much attention to the evolution of the adult form. This has, in large part, been unavoidable, since most of the fossil remains recovered have been those of adults. Abbie[70] has pointed out that it is not really a sound procedure to attempt to trace human evolution by the comparison of adult forms, and suggests that the only common stem that can be found for the primates in such an embryonic series could produce a sufficiently generalized precursor of man. Consequently, it would not be necessary to go very far back in primate history to find the ancestral form. And, as Abbie states, "If a common generalized foetal form could be discovered the problem of man's ancestry would be much closer to solution than it is now. . . ." As a working hypothesis he visualizes such a form as resembling a human embryo of about 7-weeks gestation, as shown in Fig. 26. Development at that stage is that of a generalized primate, with the digits of the hands differentiated but not those of the feet, so that there is not yet any indication whether the great toe will become lined up with the other toes as in man or will become apposable as in the apes. All that is required at this stage is a very small change in order to shift this structure either in the one or the other direction.

In Fig. 27, Abbie has provided a simple scheme to illustrate the manner in which distinctive forms of the various primates may have been derived from a common primate fetal ancestor by a combination of the processes of fetalization and gerontomorphism. Gerontomorphism is the process of phylogenetic change as the result of the modification of adult

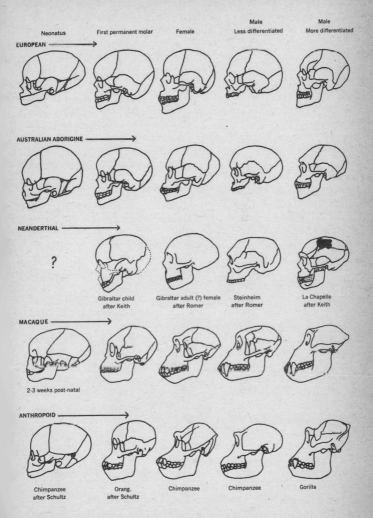

FIG. 26 From left to right, showing how the skull in the newborn of various primates differentiates to various degrees of adult ancestral form (gerontomorphism) from a relatively common newborn form. To facilitate comparison, the skulls are all drawn to approximately the same size. (*Courtesy of A. A. Abbie and the Royal Society of South Australia.*)

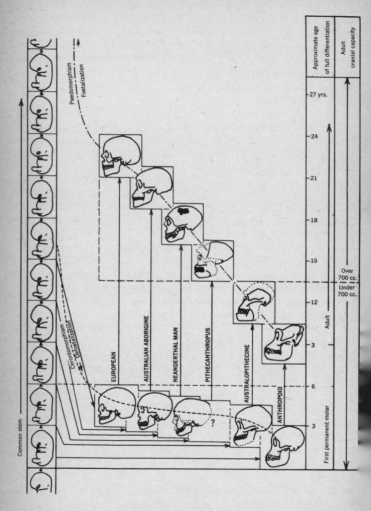

FIG. 27 A scheme to illustrate the suggested common primate stem, and the manner in which distinctive primates have been derived from it by a combination of the processes of the retention of juvenile traits in the adult forms (pedomorphism) and also the retention of ancestral adult traits (gerontomorphism). (*Courtesy of A. A. Abbie and the Royal Society of South Australia.*)

traits, by means of adult variation, whereby adult ancestral traits become the traits of youthful descendants. Development from the common stem by defetalization or gerontomorphism of varying degrees leads through such juvenile forms to those shown in the lower row in Fig. 27, which in turn lead to the gerontomorphic forms shown above, but which progressively exhibit, above the 700 cc. cranial capacity in the adult, a tendency toward the preservation of fetal traits in the adult.

The fact that man belongs to an order of mammals in which its members normally produce a single offspring at a birth (monotocous) made possible the establishment of mutations favoring fetalization. In animals that produce several young at a birth (polytocous) competition between the intrauterine organisms for nourishment and space is considerable. Under such conditions the adaptive advantage lies with rapid development, and the emergence of fetalization becomes impossible because genes favoring a slowing down of development would be eliminated. With one offspring at a birth the case is quite different, and a deceleration of development becomes a real possibility and a considerable advantage. The longer the single offspring is preserved in the womb, the more leisured its development can be, and the more likely it is to be preserved for the species. A fetus is, on the whole, better nourished and less exposed to danger than is the newborn infant, who, as we have already pointed out, is comparatively vulnerable because of the immature state in which he is born. Under the conditions of life of man's precursors and of early man himself, such a prolongation of the intrauterine period of development would have been of great advantage. Therefore, genes favoring such a prolongation of intrauterine development by a deceleration of the rate of fetal development would gradually have been established as part of the human genetic constitution by natural selection. However, the duration of the intrauterine period is only slightly, if at all, longer in man than it is in the apes. But man, as we have seen, is a special case whose gestation period must be completed in the womb of the family. Intrauterine is extended to extrauterine, to familial, gestation.

The essential feature of human evolution by neoteny has been the development of new characters by the retention of embryonic, fetal, and infantile ones. It is of interest to note that the human female exhibits this trait rather more markedly than does the male.

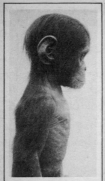 

FIG. 28 Chimpanzee juvenile and adult, the one showing a remarkable likeness to both the human child and the human adult, and the other showing the fully developed anthropoid traits.

Neoteny and the Evolution of the Human Mind

It is clear that the period of structural development in man has been appreciably extended as compared with the duration of that period in apes. It would appear that a similar process was associated with the development of those structural elements which form the physical bases of mind. In other words, as a consequence of neotenous mutations having multiple effects, both morphological characters and functional capacities may have been influenced in the hominid-human direction. On the other hand, the mutations for the strictly morphological changes, and those affecting the mental faculties, may have occurred quite independently. One thing seems highly probable: the shift to the human mental status occurred as the result of mutations which caused the retention of the capacity for educability, so characteristic of the juvenile ape, right into the adolescent and/or adult phases of development. Among other things we see this in the retention and development of the capacity to play and in the continuing growth and development of curiosity, traits which juvenile apes exhibit but lose as they mature.

Not many structural changes would have been necessary to produce those qualitative changes that would serve to differentiate the human from the ape mind. It would appear, on the other hand, that the principal, if not the only, changes necessary would be those facilitating complex symbol usage. What the nature of these changes may be is at present conjectural. Increase in the number of cerebral neurons and in the fine connections between them, with increased capacity for growth and development, resulting in more complex circuits, and in the improvement in the association, scanning, and feedback capacities of the brain, is one possibility. The late Professor E. L. Thorndike once wrote that "in their deeper nature the higher forms of intellectual operation are identical with mere association or connection forming, depending upon the same sort of physiological connections but requiring many more of them." This is, possibly, an oversimplification. However we may describe the structural changes which have undoubtedly taken place in the human brain, they will amount to but the other aspect of what has already been said, namely, that the difference between the human and the ape brain is probably based on a very small number of gene changes in the direction of a greater increase in educability. Indeed, educability is the species characteristic of man. The juvenile ape is more educable than the adult ape, and the suggestion here is that the preservation of the educability of the juvenile ape into the adult stage in man, by neoteny, serves at least in part to explain the evolution of a brain capable of a human mind.

The theory outlined in this section suggests that the shift from the status of ape to the status of human being was the result, in large part, of neotenous mutations which produced a retention of the growth trends of the juvenile brain and its potentialities for learning in the adolescent and adult phases of development. It is clear that the nature of these potentialities for learning must also have undergone intrinsic change, for no amount of extension of the ape's capacity for learning would yield a human mind.

It is further suggested that evolution by neoteny of the mental faculties has been a gradual process from the commencement of man's origin from the apes. It is questionable whether the shift from the ape to the hominid status was saltatory either for morphological or for mental traits. It may be doubted, for example, that *Homo erectus robustus* was as intelligent as Neanderthal man, though it is probable that he was more intelligent than any of the australopithecines. But even of this we cannot be certain. The progressive increase in the volume of the brain in the fossil hominids seems to have been paralleled by a progressive increase in mental capacities.

Size of brain seems to have stabilized itself in man; in fact, there seems to have been a decline in gross size or dimensions of the human brain since the days of Neanderthal man. This does not, however, mean that the increase in brain mass has come to an end. Increase in mass may be achieved by deepening and multiplication of the number of cerebral convolutions, that is, by increasing the surface area of the brain without increasing its size. There is no reason to suppose that either the quality or duration of man's capacity for learning will not be subject to further evolution. It should be understood that neoteny represents a developmental mechanism which under certain evolutionary conditions becomes available for exploitation by a population for which it is of adaptive value. It is only one such mechanism, an important one certainly, for it helps us to understand much that would otherwise remain obscure. However, for neoteny to be called into action in the evolution of any group, there must be a selective pressure for the necessary neotenous changes. Clearly, the development of the peculiar form of the breast in the human female is not a neotenous change, nor is the adoption of the erect posture, nor is the development of beard and mustache in males, to mention but a few traits. The way in which neoteny might be "called upon" to produce physical change in a population may be illustrated by the manner in which man came to lose his body hair. This is discussed on pp. 145–148. Here we may turn to a discussion of the adoption of the erect posture and other physical characteristics of man.

Physical Characteristics and Their Significance

Erect Posture and Bipedal Locomotion

The australopithecines are the earliest known primates to have achieved bipedal locomotion in the erect posture—undoubtedly in adaptation to life on the open savannas. The advantage of the erect posture is that it affords greater versatility and range of movement. On the open plains it is desirable not only to stand erect in order to be able to scan a wider horizon, but to stalk, walk, and run in that position, and at the same time to maintain the hands free for carrying, throwing, and similar acts while moving. Activities of this sort contributed to the need for and development of tools and implements which the quadrupedal primate would simply never require. The manufacture and manipulation of tools would contribute to the selection of those individuals with the necessary manipulative and related abilities, and, hence, with the almost certainly associated genes for the erect posture and bipedalism. The development of the bipedal erect posture was a master adaptation, because it required and led to the development of other correlated adaptations, which substantively contributed to the development of man's cultural capacities.

Vision, hands, the erect posture, and the manufacture of tools have reciprocally interacted and undergone evolution together. As Spuhler has pointed out, with the adoption of the upright posture vision gained a superior control of manipulation; it became *super*vision, a guide and control of fine manipulation.[71] Life on the savannas put an increasing premium upon sharpness of vision, upon the ability to scan the horizon and see what there was to see, what one needed to see, and toolmaking increasingly put a high selective value upon refinement of vision as the manipulatory skills became more complex and efficient. Seeing, for man, is an intellectual process. There is no meaningful perception without learning. We learn to rely upon our perceptions through experiencing their consequences in action. Hence, the enormous increase in the varieties of perceptual experience, brought about by the new way of life on the savannas, served to stimulate the more complex usage of the tools of mentation. The experiment implied in all critical observation, the weighing of alternative paths of action, the implicit preparation to respond involved in all perception, the scanning of the savannas for food, the sighting and tracking down of game, the stalking, walking, and running involved, the solving of the problems presented by the rapid invention of the means to their efficient solution—all this, and much else, produced an integrative action upon the increasingly interrelated development of vision, hands, the erect posture, and the invention, manufacture, and manipulation of tools—mental and material. The combination of tactile and visual patterns of experience resulting from the concentration upon the manipulation of tools in the manufacture of tools has served not only to produce a close association in development of these two senses, but also to contribute to the development of the skillful use of mental processes. The storage of experience derived from the variety of tasks performed by the hands undoubtedly served to activate and foster the development of association and other areas of the brain. The premium on such educable brains would have been very high. Under the pressure of the necessity of inventiveness, the ingenuity necessary to meet the challenges of the environment, dependence upon biologically determined bodily functions gradually declines, and comes more and more under the domination of mind—the human mind, which basically represents the cultural organization of neurogenetic potentialities. And as we have already seen, there has been a continuous feedback between cultural invention and appropriately adaptive genetic changes.

The erect posture not only contributed, by freeing the hands, to the development of tools, but also made it possible to carry things. Carrying objects of various sorts in the hands and arms contributes to the development of foresight and planning. Objects are carried with some end in view, for some purpose, and in so doing it was undoubtedly found that those objects could be applied to the meeting of other, unforeseen, challenges. As man sharpened his tools he sharpened his wits, and this he could only do with hands that had been completely freed from the necessities of locomotion. Tools as the whetstones of man's wit are intimately linked with the skillful development of the hands and the precision and fineness of vision. The manufacture of a tool implies a purpose for which it is to be used, and that purpose may entail the carrying of the tool, or the material from which the tool may be made, to a distant place where the end for which it was designed may be achieved, and without which it could not. The development of man's tools, as Napier has shown, reflects the development of man's skill and the development of his hands, from power to precision (Figs. 17 and 18).

The upright posture also means that the child can be carried by the mother in her arms in the face-to-face position, a position which affords abundant opportunities for mutual scanning and intercommunication. The recognition not only of the mobile facial expressions of the mother, but also their meaning, and the meaning also of those proprioceptive messages which are conveyed to the infant in its mother's arms by the manner in which she holds it. It is in this face-to-face position that she feeds the child and talks to it. It is in this position that it learns the well-nigh universal head motion, at the breast, for "yes," and also the head motion for "no" in refusing the breast.[72]

With the adoption of the erect posture, not only did the pelvic bones and its appendages undergo rearrangement, but so did the pelvic outlet. This was accompanied by a more forward placement of the vagina and external genitalia in the human female. Even in the infant female apes I have examined the vagina and external genitalia are situated somewhat more posteriorly than they are in the human female. The more anterior position of the external genitalia together with the upright posture made the face-to-face position during coitus more comfortable than the posterior approach usually practiced by the apes. The consequences of the adoption of face-to-face coitus were considerable. Male and female were brought not only more closely together physically but also psychologically. In the face-to-face position they would learn to embrace each other, to exhibit tender emotions toward each other, and to invent kissing, nose-rubbing, caressing, and similar forms of behavior—which would then be extended to others, particularly to children in everyday situations.

The foot of man, adapted to the erect posture, is a miracle of engineering. No one who has not dissected that astonishingly beautiful complex of systems we call the human foot can ever understand what a marvel it is. It was probably the hunting way of life that played the most important role in the evolution of the human foot—for it is in running that the foot exhibits virtually all those functions which so peculiarly characterize it. The feet of anthropoids are a combination of grasping and leverage devices—grasping in the trees, levers for locomotion on the ground. In apes the functional axis of the foot runs between the first and second metatarsals. On the ground this functional axis becomes the "leverage axis," and the heads of the first and second metatarsal bones serve as the fulcrum of leverage action. In the apes the big toe is widely divergent from the other toes and set low upon the foot. This is desirable in a grasping foot. With the adoption of terrestrial life, and especially the practice of running, leverage action gradually supplanted the grasping function of the foot. The erect posture was associated with a transfer of the foot's leverage action to its inner border, an action which is particularly associated with running. During running body weight is balanced upon the leverage axis, throughout the period of ground contact, because the heel is elevated by the calf muscles, since in running it does not establish contact with the ground. During both walking and running,

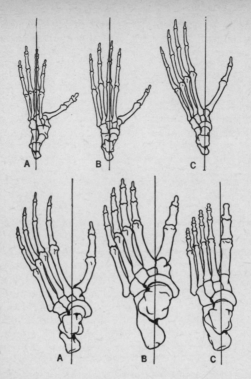

FIG. 29   Location of the functional axis of the foot in monkeys, apes, and man. Upper row: the primitive type of functional axis as shown in the lemur (*Lepidolemur*), *A*, and the monkey (Macaque), *B*, types of feet; also the inward displacement of the functional axis in the gibbon, *C*, the most primitive of living anthropoid apes. Lower row: foot bones of the chimpanzee, *A;* the gorilla, *B;* and man, *C*, showing increased development along the inner border of the foot and more massive heel, as a result of terrestrial specialization. (*From Morton.*)

half the weight of the body is supported by the big toe in man; this is not so in the apes, in which the weight is distributed between the other toes. The characteristic longitudinal arch of man is also a result of remodelling in adaptation to the erect posture, and especially to running. The deflection of body weight to the inner border of the foot at the end of the stride or takeoff, and the forces from the ball of the foot as well as the accessory propulsive forces from the toes in running, producing propulsive and gravitational thrusts, are sufficient to lift and propel the body during the interval when both feet are off the ground. It is this combination of forces which is responsible for the longitudinal arches. In running, the toes are brought strongly against the ground at the beginning of contact, unlike the situation in walking. The interaction between the forces of gravity and the propulsive efforts of the muscles, especially in running, was the designing agency in producing the human longitudinal arch.[73] Walking and standing helped to shape the human foot, but it was running that was its chief architect. As Weston La Barre has remarked, man stands alone because he alone stands.

The Buttocks

Well developed buttocks are a peculiar trait of man. None of the other primates has anything so well developed. The projection called the buttocks or rump, in man, is largely due to the massive development of the gluteus maximus as a consequence of the adoption of the erect posture. While other muscles of the pelvis and lower extremity have been significantly involved in the evolution of the erect posture, it is the gluteus maximus which has been most affected. It is the muscle that contracts to extend the hip joint, in running, climbing, ascending steps, raising the trunk from the stooping or sitting position, and relaxes under tension as these positions are assumed. It is critical in maintaining balance of the trunk upon the femur and of the femur upon the tibia (through the iliotibial tract) in holding the erect posture.

The gluteus maximus is, in fact, the heaviest and coarsest fibered muscle of the body, and by its weight contributes to form the buttock. However, a great part of the projection and rounded form of the buttock is contributed by the deposit of fat in the superficial fascia. The fold of the buttock, for example, is formed by this fatty padding and not by the lower border of the gluteus maximus. The thickness of the gluteal fat varies considerably in different individuals, but it is always present.

I am going to suggest here that the form of the buttocks in man is not wholly due to the adoption of the erect posture, but is in part also due to the adoption of the horizontal posture when sleeping. I am proposing that the form of the buttocks in man represents, in part, an adaptation to man's adoption of the habit of lying on the ground to sleep. No other primate does so, unless forced by the absence of other facilities.

Monkeys sleep in trees, and apes sleep in temporary nests they build either in or at the foot of trees. With man's adoption of a fully terrestrial way of life, sleeping on the ground would be extremely hard on the body surfaces in contact with it. The development of thickened skin, and/or adipose tissue, and possibly even muscle, would serve to cushion the underlying structures against excessive pressure. I suggest that the buttocks serve as the pillows of the pelvis, whether one lies on one's back or on one's side.

In whatever position one lies, the surfaces of the body bearing the greatest pressures are the buttocks, the shoulders, the sides of the face and head, and the back of the head. In adaptation to the pressures produced during sleep on these parts of the body, it is of interest to note that the skin is thickest in the shoulder region, that the parts of the face and head most padded with fat are the sides of the face and head, the front of the face and head being notably comparatively free of fat, and that the back and sides of the head are provided with hair, and the back of the head with muscle, ligament, and fat. The beard in males may also, in part, serve to cushion the face less endowed with fat than that of the female.

The adoption of the erect posture has contributed to the greater muscularization of the gluteal region and to the relative lordosis resulting from the development of a more marked lumbosacral curvature, both factors which have promoted the development of the kind of buttocks peculiar to man.

The excessive development of the buttocks among Bushmen and Hottentots is due to the deposit of fat, and probably has no connection whatever with cushioning functions. The Bushman has one of the lowest total body adiposity coefficients of any people in the world,[74] and the highest development of steatopygia. Sexual selection has been offered as one explanation. But most authorities are agreed that sexual selection in man cannot have played a significant role during the major part of man's evolution. A frequent suggestion has been that such "morphological bustles" serve as reserve food depots during periods of sparsity, akin to the humps of the camel and dromedary and the fat tails of certain sheep. There is no evidence whatever in support of this latter theory. I suggest here that steatopygia is principally an adaptation to the unique habitat in which the Bushman has evolved, a habitat of great heat and aridity necessitating an adaptive reduction in general body fat in order to permit rapid heat loss, while maintaining a sufficient amount of fat for normal metabolic purposes, especially in an environment which may grow very cold at night. Hence, the reduction of general body fat and its relegation to an unobtrusive part of the body, where it serves as a depot for general utilization by the body.

While the gluteal structures serve a cushioning function in sitting, the pressure upon them of the ischial tuberosities cannot be sustained for too long a period of time. Monkeys and some apes, who do a great deal of sitting and sleeping in the sitting posture, have developed ischial callosities. Man has developed subgluteal and subcutaneous ischial bursae, but these are insufficient to protect him against pressure discomfort following upon prolonged sitting. Prolonged sitting is physiologically hazardous, hence ischial pressure discomfort may have positive selective value in encouraging activity designed to avoid cardiovascular stress.

Within and between ethnic groups there is considerable variability in the size and form of the buttocks, and in females they are generally more developed than in males. Interestingly enough, the buttocks are relatively more developed in infants than in older children or in young adults. The greater development of the buttocks in infants is probably related to the fact that they spend so much time lying on their backs and sides. In correlation the shoulder-scapula region is also well padded. After middle age, especially in women, the accumulation of fat appears to have a selective preference for the buttocks, resulting in so-called "middle-age spread."

Man's Hairlessness

Man is characterized by a glabrousness (hairlessness) which stands in marked contrast to the thick pelage which covers the bodies of most other primates, especially of the great apes. The reduction in man's body hair almost certainly followed upon the adoption of the erect posture and a new way of life resulting in certain physiological changes which favored survival and perpetuation of genotypes for reduced hair. It also appears to have been of adaptive advantage for hair to remain, and even to increase in density, on certain parts of the body, such as the head, eyebrows, beard, pubic and perineal regions, and axilla (armpit). In what manner could these changes have been brought about?

For the answer to this question we must once again look to the hunting way of life on the open savannas. In hunting much running is necessary, and the chase may extend over hours and even days. Under such conditions, in a torrid environment, the body will become heated. Overheating is dangerous and can be lethal. That man was originally a tropical animal is strongly indicated, among other things, by the fact that his normal body temperature is 98.6° Fahrenheit. His comfort zone for external temperature is between 65° and 95° F. Man tolerates heat better than cold, but by the use of culturally developed devices he is capable of living under all climatic conditions, from the pole of cold to the summers of Philadelphia.

The new way of life which hunting entailed meant that some means of eliminating the body heat generated during the hunt was vitally necessary. Indeed, what was even more important was the development of some mechanism by which the body could protect itself against heat accumulation, and not merely as an emergency device for its elimination. This is most effectively achieved by sweating. Forest-dwelling animals generally do not possess sweat glands; the air by which they are surrounded is heavily saturated with moisture, and this, together with their habit of avoiding overheating and prolonged exposure to heat, is more than adequate to protect them against its effects. The great apes, for example, normally proceed about their activities at a leisurely pace, and spend much of their time at rest or in sleep. Sweat glands, in apes, are not well developed. The gorilla, the chimpanzee, and to a lesser extent the orang-utan, do have a mixture of both eccrine and apocrine glands in their armpits, but on the whole their sweat glands are less developed than in man.[75] "Man," on the other hand, as Professor Yas Kuno writes, "occupies the premier position in the animal kingdom in respect to the development of the sweat apparatus. There are many animals provided with the sweat apparatus, but there is none who shows such a vivid sweat response as does man."[76] Usually, on a hot day, the only animals at the zoo likely to be seen sweating are the visitors outside the cages and enclosures. There is, however, one exception, namely, the rhinoceros. The rhinoceros, like man, is virtually hairless and has a good layer of fat beneath the skin. When it becomes overheated by running it sweats prodigiously. It may well be that it is the heat-insulating layer of fat which makes such efficient sweating necessary in both animals. Man sweats from every part of his body surface, having about 750 sweat glands to each square inch of skin.

It was the hunting way of life which almost certainly re-

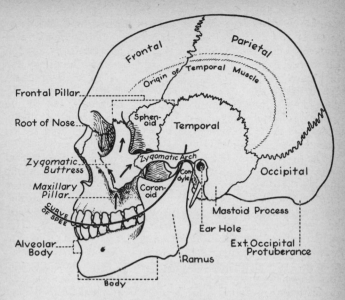

FIG. 30 Lateral view of the human skull.

sulted in the development, in man, of the largest number of sweat glands to be found in any animal, a system of sweat glands capable of producing amounts of sweat over the body surface up to a maximum of 2 liters or more than 2 quarts per hour! This would amount to the removal of 1200 calories per hour from the body, and a lowering of the temperature of the body by 68° Fahrenheit. The temperature regulation of the body by sweating could hardly, therefore, be more efficiently performed. The common complaint in hot weather is of too much sweat. As Professor Kuno writes, "The maximal rate of sweating seems to be that required to maintain constancy of body temperature in outdoor life under hot sunshine" (p. 341). This is the kind of life that man has led during the whole of his history, with only a few exceptions arising during the very recent period. Hunting still remains the major way of life of the greater number of peoples who have not yet been wholly affected by civilization. In any event, massive sweating is incompatible with a heavy growth of body hair, and because of this incompatibility, it is here suggested, man became the only reduced-hair member of the primates, hair of some density being retained only where it served an adaptively useful purpose.

To summarize, then, as a consequence of the hunting way of life, entailing much and prolonged exercise, an extensive system of sweat glands was developed as a mechanism for reducing the resulting body heat through the evaporation of the excreted sweat which carries off the accumulated heat. A heavy coat of hair would have the precisely opposite effect of conserving the accumulated heat, hence, the selection pressure would be toward reduction in both the density and length of hair. The ability to live in torrid zones, and indeed to spread to their farthest reaches, was made possible by the evolution, in man, of the most highly developed system of sweat glands in the whole animal kingdom, and the concomitant reduction of body hair. Where hair was of adaptive value, it was retained; where it was not, it was reduced. We may now turn, then, to a consideration of the possible conditions responsible for the retention of hair in certain parts of the body.

Head Hair

The adaptive value of head hair apparently lies in the protection it affords against physical injury from accidental blows, lacerations, and scratches, from overheating from sunlight, and from overcooling by cold. Bald men speak with the greatest authority on this subject. The scalp has no insulating layer of fat beneath the skin. The aponeurosis of the fronto-occipitalis muscle, which stretches from the forehead over the top to the back of the head, provides no cushioning whatever against physical blows, no absorptive medium for heat, and no protection against cold. A layer of hair provides all these.

Eyebrows

Eyebrows are also found situated over a region without a fatty cushion, and as a substitute for the subjacent bony eyebrow ridges of apes provide an external cushion in the form of particularly thick hairs which serve to protect the delicate supraorbital margins from injury. In heavy sweating from the forehead the eyebrows serve to prevent the sweat from descending into the eyes, just as the hair on the top of the head similarly serves to hold the scalp sweat from descending.

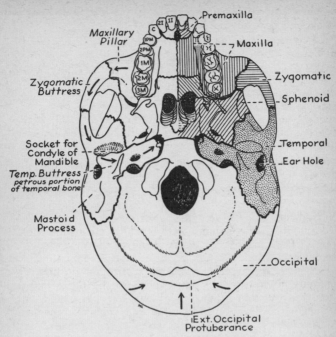

FIG. 31   Basal view of the human skull.

The Beard

The great variation in beardedness among different populations of man suggests that different adaptive mechanisms may
well have been responsible for the range of variation from
virtually complete beardlessness, as among Bushmen, to very
heavy beardedness, as among Caucasoids. In cold regions a
beard certainly affords protection against freezing, but leaves
the nose and ears liable to be frostbitten. In very cold regions
a more efficient adaptive response would be development of
faces well padded with fat, as is the case in the Eskimo and
some other Mongoloid peoples. Negroid peoples, in general,
are sparsely endowed with beards, and this perhaps is connected with adaptation to a high-sunlight, high-temperature
habitat and ease of sweating.

Beard and mustache may well have the same adaptive

value as eyebrows and head hair, namely, as a protective pad against injury to the delicate facial bones, the tooth-bearing parts of the jaws, and the cartilages at the front of the neck. In light-skinned individuals they may also serve as protection against excessive exposure to sunlight. Women, as comparatively sedentary creatures removed from the dangers of the hunt, would not require such a protective growth and so would not develop it.

Pubic and Perineal Hair

Pubic hair in man differs in form, structure, and quantity in the sexes. In both sexes, however, the hair in this region may serve the same functions. The first of these is the protection of the skin from chafing as a consequence of movements in intercourse, and the second is enhancement of sexual excitation in the same manner as tactile hairs contribute to the sensation of touch. The development of the mons veneris in the female would appear to represent an adaptation to the assumption of the male's superior horizontal position in intercourse in relation to the female's supine horizontal position, the function of the underlying adipose tissue being to prevent excessive pressure on the bony pubis of the female.

The form of the hair on the mons of the female is usually curly or crinkly and short, and thus forms a far more effective pad than if it were straight. This represents a really striking example of adaptive response. In the male the pubic hair is straight or wavy, and the thickness of each hair is greater than it is in any other part of the body, being four times the thickness of head hair. The delicate scrotal sac of the male is afforded protection from chafing against the medial aspects of the thighs. In this region, especially in sitting or squatting, the dependent hairs may be seen to be relatively thickly packed between scrotum and thigh. Similarly, in the female the long hairs descend mostly over the region of the clitoris and grow on the labia majora, but not on the labia minora, and on the inner aspect of the thigh in the area between the labia majora and the medial aspect of the thigh. The function of the long hairs here is clearly to protect the skin against chafing.

A similar protection against chafing is afforded by the perineal hair, in the region between the thighs from the coccyx to the pubis (embracing the anus and external genitalia).

With the termination of reproductive life, women, and to some extent men, tend to lose much of their pubic hair.

Axillary Hair

The hair in the armpits (axillae) constitutes an excellent example of the function of hair as a buffer against chafing. The many movements of the arm made during the course of a day in a region abundantly supplied with sweat glands, prolonged over a considerable period, would result in some discomfort at the least, and in morbid changes at the worst. Another function of axillary hair would appear to be the facilitation of movements of the arm, as anyone who has ever had his axillary hair clipped will know. Under hunting conditions an armpit free of hair would become sticky instead of oily, as the hairy axilla does, and thus impede efficient movement of the arm. Axillary hair also facilitates sweating from the abundantly present axillary sweat glands. The hair also facilitates the decomposition of the sweat by the bacteria which live on it. Finally, axillary sweat is said to have a considerable sexual attractiveness, and this, too, may not be without some significance for the persistence of hair within the axilla.

General Persisting Body Hair

Among nonliterate peoples who habitually wear little or no clothing, sensory acuity of the skin is markedly more highly developed than it is among peoples that habitually wear clothes. Insects alighting upon the skin are first likely to announce the fact through the disturbance they set up at the base of a hair follicle, which, passing its transmittor substance along the course of a sensory nerve to the central nervous system, at once initiates the desirable protective response. Adequately distributed body hairs, therefore, remain, to serve the function of antennae which pick up any disturbances at the base of the hair follicle and then convert them into the proper message. Body hair, among other things, serves, then, as a sensory warning device alerting the individual to the arrival upon his body of insects and similar creatures, which can then be dealt with before they do any harm.

Territoriality, Migration, and Differentiation

The wide distribution of the australopithecines over southern and eastern Africa tells us that they prospered and multiplied. As numbers increased and the natural resources were put under an increasing toll, the pressure for subsistence would cause families or a group of families to migrate from the ancestral territory to adjacent areas. In this manner the range of the australopithecines would have become greatly extended. In this manner, also, small populations of australopithecines occupying a particular territory would come to regard it as their own, their homeland, and to defend it against any threatened incursions by other groups. Defense, not so much against attack, of which we modern men are so prone to think, but against the temporary invasion of hunting rights, in other words, against trespassing. Such defense would take the form not of armaments, but of elaborate patterns of social regulations clearly understood by everyone whose conception of his own territorial rights was similar.

The isolation of distance or other natural barriers between separate populations of australopithecines would, in the course of time, as a result of the operation of the evolutionary factors of isolation, mutation, natural selection, genetic drift (the random driftage of genes), and social selection, result in differentiation of such populations. Hence, the varieties of australopithecines.

Among those groups occupying adjacent territories, while territorial separateness would be maintained and respected, visiting between groups and hybridization between members of the adjacent groups would occur. Physical and cultural likenesses would tend to be greater between such adjacent groups than between groups distantly removed from each other. With the continuing operation of such factors over the course of many scores of thousands of years man, as we know him in all his varieties, was ultimately evolved.

Epilogue

We have dealt in this book with that "moment" in time when those events occurred which transformed an ape into a man. We have considered the evidence which tells us what the conditions were that led to that transformation. It is an exciting and illuminating story. Man emerges from that story a creature of heroic proportions, a made-over ape who may justly take pride in his ancestry and in the achievements of his forebears.

Man shows himself to advantage as a creature of great adaptability. A creature who accepted the challenge of the brave new world in which he found himself, and responded to it so successfully that he finally mastered it. Incorporating stress and strain into his very being as a part of the changing environment, which he must accept and to which he must adapt. Man as man must remain eternally vigilant, protecting and cherishing, as he grows in humanity, the qualities which have brought him to this high estate. These qualities he holds in trust for future generations.

From the very birth of man as a new species we observe that he developed a complex of behavioral traits which interoperatively acted and reacted upon each other in a feedback relation, almost every cultural advance eliciting a genetic response, and every genetic response putting a selective pressure upon the individual to meet the changes to which such responses gave rise. These traits, the growth of intelligence, practical, rational, and speculative, the concomitant loss of instincts, the predisposition to *react* replaced by the disposition to *respond*, the prolongation of the dependency period, the lengthening of every stage of postnatal development, infancy, childhood, adolescence, maturity, and old age, the ability to cooperate, the increase in educability, the growth of love, inventiveness, and toolmaking, these are man's basic functional traits. And out of them grow a great many others.

Educability, plasticity, and adaptability, all words for much the same trait, have from the very beginning of man's history been the qualities which have distinguished him. His cultural and genetic evolution have proceeded interdigitatively, hand-in-hand together. As we have seen, almost every cultural ad-

153

vance elicited a genetic response, and every genetic change placed a new selective pressure on the individual to meet the challenges to which such genetic changes gave rise. In this manner culture has constituted the principal selective agency which has produced and directed the changes in the genetic constitution of evolving man to his present genetic state. This process continues at this very moment, with one substantial difference. That difference arises from the fact that today, in the Western world, we are buffering the effect of natural selection for millions of individuals who, under the conditions of a food-gathering and hunting economy, would have had no chance of surviving. Having learned to control death by making survival possible for millions of human beings who would otherwise have died in infancy or at later ages, we have not yet learned to control birth, with the result that we have complicated out of all proportion virtually every problem with which human beings and with which humanity as a whole are confronted. The population explosion threatens to destroy us all by its fallout. And yet we have the knowledge, and some have the foresight to use that knowledge in the hope that by so doing others may also be persuaded of the dangers of overpopulation. For this, overpopulation, is man's present greatest hazard. Overpopulation threatens to overwhelm and debase the quality of humanity, as nothing else has hitherto succeeded in doing.

When men lived in small bands the very smallness of the population contributed to the possibility of each individual's fulfillment as a person. But today the person, even in the so-called affluent society, loses himself in the mass. It is the rare individual who rises above it. Most individuals are almost literally engulfed by the pressures of their society in a sea of oblivioning anonymity. Self-identity is weakened and often lost. This was not always so, and it is not a desirable condition for any individual or for humanity. In the early history of man every individual's worth was established by his very existence, for the fact that he had surmounted the dangers of birth and successfully met the challenges of a harsh and refractory environment constituted sufficient testimony to his worth. This, indeed, was the "judgment" of natural selection validated by social recognition. Each individual, from child to adult, was a recognized member of society, whose personality, skills, kinship relations, age grade, status, and individuality were distinguished with respect and unambiguous appreciation. These are the traits, among others, that are explicitly and clearly recognized in relation to the individual in every nonliterate society to this day, and there can be little doubt that this was so among the earliest societies of man.

The recognition and cultivation of individuality have the greatest survival value, for what is achieved by these means is the binding of the person increasingly more closely to the group, and reciprocally adaptive favoring of both the individual and the group. In this process the individual becomes more of a person and less of an individualist. Initiation rites are designed to recognize formally the passage of the member of the group from one class of responsibilities into a broader class of responsibilities and obligations, from a less mature to a more mature stage of development. Such rites are called *rites of passage*. Often these rites take the form of rebirth ceremonies, in which the initiate has vividly impressed upon him the nature of his own responsibilities, and the group in this way ceremonially recognizes and validates the worthiness of its newly reborn and revitalized member. Everyone is responsible to everyone for everyone. It is a very different world from that in which we live, in which everyone is responsible for himself to himself and, outside the members of his immediate family, to no one else. This development is in large part due, I suspect, to the structure of the Christian family in the Western world. The family, in the Christian world, is so structured as to focus attention upon the development of the individualism, *not* the individuality, of each of its members. The Christian family of the Western world is an atomized unit, only tenuously associated with the like units in the community. What that family teaches is concentration on self, selfishness, egotheism, atomism, apartness, and dissociation. The trend in this direction appears to have begun with the development of urbanization, some six or more thousand years ago.[77] It is a development which is in opposition to the best interests of man, for man is by nature a cooperative creature, who needs to do for others what others should be doing for him. Man, as we have seen, has developed as a cooperative, loving, intelligent, dependent, interdependent, instinctless, educable, plastic creature. All these traits have evolved in reciprocal interdependence with one another, hand-in-hand, in a feedback relation.

With the loss of instincts and the increasing development of intelligence there went a concomitant development of dependency, interdependency, and love. Without the growth and development of love sex would have remained the fulfillment of lust, of carnality, and intelligence would have evolved as mere cunning. But with the development of love sexual fulfillment has resulted in the biological family, in conjugal love, and in love of children. Without love intelligence would have bred innumerable tyrants; but with love to control intelligence, fraternal love, man has used it to better the lot of his fellow man. Without love intelligence is dangerous; without intelligence love is not enough. In the evolution of man each has fed the other, as one hand washes the other. Intelligence and love have evolved in feedback relation with one another—the dissociation of the one from the other always spelling danger. Without the control of love, self-preservation would have been the dominant motive of behavior. With love the preservation of the group is supreme. Love is simply defined as behavior calculated to confer survival benefits upon others in a creatively enlarging manner. The value of love and cooperation must have been quickly recognized by early man, and since such behavior contributed both to the survival of the individual and the group it would have had a high selective value. Today we know, as a result of many independent investigations, that love is the most important of all the needs which requires satisfaction if human beings are to grow and develop adequately.[78] Mental health, indeed, is the ability to love, for love is the essential human relationship. As William Watson wrote in "The Hope of the World":

> Did Heaven vouchsafe some sign
>   That through all Nature's frame
> Boundless ascent benign
>   Is everywhere her aim,
> Such as man hopes it here,
>   Where he from beasts hath risen,—
> Then might I read full clear,
>   Ev'n in my sensual prison,
> That Life and Law and Love are one
>   Symphonius name.

Love has not generally been considered a factor of human evolution, any more than mutual aid or cooperation were until very recently.[79] But the evidence of man's early evolution, as we have been able to reconstruct it, all points to the fact that love has been a powerful factor in the evolution of man. With the great extension of the dependency period of the child, the capacity to minister to its increasing dependency needs has been under continuous selection pressure in females primarily and in males secondarily. It should not be surprising, then, that love constitutes the most powerful of all of man's culturally developed needs.

Wherever man's conduct, whether individual, group, or institutionalized, is informed by love and compassion there we perceive at work the evolutionary factor which, together with intelligence, has been and will always continue to be the most important in the continuing evolution of man.

Intelligence is a great deal more than a merely valuable intellectual quality. It is, in fact, a necessity of healthy development. Thinking is an ability as essential for health as it is for survival. It has brought man a long way on an immense journey. It was at one time an ability in which everyone was vitally concerned. This, unfortunately, is no longer so. In the recent period we have reserved the training in rigorous thinking for a genetically well-endowed élite, and trained the "others" in an incapacity to think. We flatter ourselves that we can make machines that think like human beings, but omit to observe that we also can make human beings who think like machines. The result is not intelligence, but its caricature. It is the travesty of thought, the perversion of man's crowning quality. When thought is mechanized it becomes stereotyped, conformist, imitative, and uncreative. It becomes anti-thought, a barrier to the reception and an impediment to the development of new ideas. We are human because we think. Mankind will always stand in need of the unconfused and unobstructed capacity to think on the part of as many as possible, not alone for the benefit of mankind but for the benefit also of the individual who remains a person. The unperson is already too much with us. Mankind's, the group's, best guarantee of creative survival is the person's trained capacity for independent thinking passed through the alembic of love. The brain is an organ of mental health and becomes the organ of mental ill-health only when it becomes disordered by a disordered conditioning in the experience of love or the lack of it and inadequate training in the ability to think. These two traits of man should never be dissociated from one another. We observe the ill-effects of such dissociation among highly intellectual individuals who, putting ideas before everything else, fail to understand that intellect without love is not enough, that, indeed, it is something less than enough, just as love without intelligence is not enough. Mankind stands in need not alone of light, but also of warmth. To love and to think, these are the two great chords of might.

We need to pay more attention to the meaning of those words than we have in the recent past.

Man's evolutionary history is highly informative. It tells us that all men have a need for participation in their community, for they are involved in one another. They have a need for creativeness, for inventiveness, for discovery, for the expression and satisfaction of curiosity. These are traits upon which the evolutionary process in man has set a high premium. These traits should not be allowed to lie fallow, uncultivated; their development should be encouraged. Man, as we have seen, came into being because his ancestors took up the challenges which confronted them and responded to them appropriately and successfully. Those responses were what transformed his ancestors into men. Those responses were mainly of a problem-solving kind. Man is a problem-solving animal, the creature that transforms accidents into opportunities. Man grows and develops by solving problems. Problem-solving is his inheritance, and humanity is the achievement which emerges from the solving of problems. The person, the personality, is, like humanity, not alone an inheritance, but an achievement for which every individual must work.

If play is the preparation in childhood for the more serious business of later life,[80, 81] work is a necessity of civilized existence. Man is a hard worker. Work is his chief source of happiness. It is the principal vehicle which made the realization of all his human traits possible. It is a habit which should be cultivated in children from their earliest years, for work is not only a necessity of civilized being, it is also an indispensable condition of mental health. As James Russell Lowell wrote:

> No man is born into the world whose work
> Is not born with him; there is always work;
> And tools to work withal. . . .

In this age of science, when the god of most men's idolatry has become the scientist, it is necessary to understand that science is far too important an activity to leave to the scientist, that man's principal problems are still the moral, the ethical, ones that have always served as the basic challenges to his capacity for cooperation. The question "Am I my brother's keeper?" could be asked only in a society in which men had ceased to be involved in one another. It could never have been asked in the earlier stages of man's social development. Man *had* to be his brother's keeper; or else there would have been no men left to tell the tale. When men cease to be their brothers' keepers, the very real danger then arises that they will altogether cease to be, for involvement in the welfare of others is the essential human relation. Without that involvement there is no humanity, but only its mask. Mankind without humanity is an anachronism, a disorder. It is a disorder, alas, which has spread widely throughout the Western world. The return to humanity is still a possibility for mankind.

In the recent period mankind has suffered many changes for the worse. There has been a progressive attrition of values, with the result that many men and women today live in a state of bewilderment, uncertain of direction, with the boundaries of right and wrong obscured, and unable to recognize the heartlessness behind the show of love.

The person is not what he is born as, for as a person he is what others have made of him, and most importantly what he has himself made of himself. We are not responsible for the errors of others, but we *are* responsible for the rectification of those errors, not alone in the community of man, but in ourselves. Just as it is true that humanity has made itself, so it will always remain true that every man has it within him, to a large extent, to be his own maker. Indeed, more significantly than that, he has it in him to be his own *re*maker. He has the capacity to undo at least some of the damage that has been done him, and to remake himself in something of the character that he ought to be. The uniqueness of man lies in the fact that whatever ideal his "ought" enshrines, man by striving possesses the capacity to realize that ideal.

Being human means working at it, and true civilization is the development of the art of being both intelligent and kind, the ability to work and the ability to love.

The human revolution lies precisely in the fact that man has evolved as the creature who has become creatively increasingly interdependent upon the need to love and be loved. Hence, the vital importance for human beings of understanding the meaning of love.

As man has grown in intelligence and in his ability to make tools, he has grown in his need for love. The cleverer man grows and the more interested in things he becomes, the more he stands in danger of himself. Love is the governor that keeps cleverness in check. When we say that man has become too clever for his own good we put it very well, for when man's cleverness outruns his goodness, his welfare, his goodness, his

very survival, are threatened. Satan was not wanting in cleverness. Indeed, Satan represents the symbol of the evil that
cleverness unregulated by love can become. Cleverness is not
enough. In the final analysis those alone are intelligent who are
able to solve not only the problems involving ideas and things,
but also the problems involving human relations. And for the
solution of human problems not only knowledge, but love,
compassion, understanding, thoughtfulness, are indispensable.
These are the necessary and sufficient conditions for human
survival.

Man has always lived in environments undergoing more or
less continuous change, and he has been a prime mover in
bringing about such changing environments. To such changes
man has always made the necessary adaptations. His environments have been changing at an acceleratingly rapid pace.
The most powerful agent of change has been man himself,
working through the medium of culture. Up to the recent
period man has done extremely well under the most challenging conditions. Owing, in part, to the very acceleration of the
process of change itself in the recent period, it has become
increasingly difficult for men to perceive the condition of man
as a whole. One of the consequences of this is that today one
adaptation man is in danger of failing to make is the recognition of his own capacity for the genesis of disaster—and its
prevention. Mankind needs to pause in its headlong rush
toward the catastrophe which is inevitable, unless the long
overdue stocktaking is undertaken. And this every man must
do for himself and enable others to do. A book such as this,
and the story it tells, can be of help only if the lessons it
teaches are clearly understood and thoroughly absorbed—and
then acted upon.

Man, it is often stated, has mastered his environment. What,
however, is often forgotten is that he is himself part of his
environment, and it is the most important part, the only part,
that he has not mastered. Man through his creation of culture
has created himself. Through the same agency he has it in his
power to create the conditions of change in the necessary
directions. Ignorance is not bliss, nor yet a negative condition
of not-knowing. Ignorance is a voluntary decision not to know.
It is a positive act of negation. The information, knowledge,
and the means by which man can control and guide his own
further development are all available, and it is nothing less
than the moral obligation of every person to make himself
acquainted with the knowledge and the means whereby he

can bring about those changes which will ensure the fulfillment and healthy development of every human being—everywhere.

As Kenneth Mather[82] has pointed out, cultural evolution does not imply genetic evolution, and may in fact conceal genetic decline. Given the fact that some members of a population possess the genetic potentials for being innovators and there exist a sufficient number of individuals within the population possessing the necessary capacity to learn from them, society can progress. Under such conditions the genetic quality of a population could steadily decline behind a façade of apparent, even accelerating, cultural progress. The danger is that this may well be occurring at the present time or occur at some future time without our being aware of it, for as Mather points out, in our modern societies we have no built-in safeguards against such a development. Indeed, most of the safeguards that did exist in earlier times have been removed. It is not that the action of natural selection has been suspended, but that it has been controlled. By cultural means enormous numbers of human beings are protected against the assaults and insults of the environment which, in earlier years, would have put a swift end to their lives. Where, formerly, the survival of the individual depended largely upon his own qualities, in modern times that function has largely been assumed by society, particularly the highly developed societies of the modern world. The buffering provided by such societies against the defects and inadequacies, physical and mental, which formerly without such buffering would have put an early end to many individuals now enables them to live to old age. The balance of the internal forces of selection has been changed, and it is no longer so much the genetic quality of the individual that counts, but the genetic quality of a few individuals who produce the cultural changes which enable the genetically less well endowed to survive and multiply.

But man's most important quality is not his capacity to survive under the buffered conditions of an aseptic environment, but the quality of his intelligence. A serious decline in the genetic quality of intelligence could endanger the existence of the whole species, for in making it possible for the genetically less well endowed to survive and reproduce there is an ever present danger that the less intelligent may vote themselves, together with the more intelligent, into situations that may prove irreversibly disastrous. This is something with which everyone who has his fellow man's welfare at heart must be concerned. In lands in which the responsibility for the welfare of the individual is increasingly being taken over by the state the pressures of natural as well as cultural selection are being changed, so that while the rate of cultural progress may be accelerating the rate of genetic decline may be progressing too.

Our genetic heritage needs to be protected, for upon its foundations all else is built. This is something that eugenists long ago recognized, but unfortunately compromised by over-zealous programs for the improvement of the species based on inadequate knowledge and too often prejudiced ideas. Some sort of controls will eventually have to be instituted to protect our genetic heritage from deterioration and impoverishment. If at the present time we appear to be behaving like thoughtless and irresponsible spendthrifts of our patrimony, it is worth remembering that we are of the species that is capable not only of perceiving the fact and of predicting its consequences, but also of taking the steps necessary to do what we ought. Genetic and cultural evolution are not mutually exclusive processes, and we must see to it that the interaction which has made possible the genetic and cultural development of man in the past continues. The culture that has been the means of making our genetic heritage possible must not become the means of its destruction.

With compassion, understanding, and involvement in the welfare of our fellow men, we must continue those researches and inquiries that will enable human beings to fulfill themselves without being genetically handicapped by the thoughtless or misguided behavior of their progenitors.

The danger faced by man is not, as some misguided eugenists feel, that his intelligence will be drastically lowered, but that it will be so highly favored that it will increase at the expense of other equally valuable traits. This is already happening. While the constructive effects of intelligence are evident, so also are its destructive effects. When intelligence is ungoverned by foresight, balance, understanding, and moral responsibility, the effects of such intelligence can be lethal.

With any sudden change in the environment the organism that has become overspecialized in any one trait, *too* fit, is likely to be at a disadvantage, compared with those organisms that have retained a more balanced general adaptability. It is the fittest, not the fit, who are in danger of extinction. This is the situation which man faces today, and unless he learns in time to understand what the consequences are of the rise in intelligence at the cost of a declining humanity, he may yet perish from this earth.

It is the struggle for fulfillment rather than the struggle for survival that we have to look to for the future, *if* we manage to survive at all. Not to mere existence, as Mellersh has written, but to a fuller existence, "not only for life but for a wider and deeper life. That must surely apply, by all the signs, to all men back to the very earliest."[83]

The story of the evolution of the varieties of man subsequent to the australopithecines has been many times told. It is the story of continuing triumphs against great odds, of revolutionary advances first achieved by the australopithecines and their forebears. It is a profoundly significant story upon which we would do well to reflect. Virtually all the elements of that adventure are present in the history of the rise of the australopithecines and their immediate forerunners; that history exhibits those elements in high relief, so that we are able to perceive clearly what the principal factors in the evolution of man have been. The post-australopithecine story need not be retold here. Man's earliest known beginnings have been the theme of the present book. Man's subsequent development is but an elaboration of that story.

References

1. James Boswell. *The Life of Samuel Johnson, LL.D.*, 2 vols. London: Henry Baldwin, 1791.

2. Léon-Paul Fargue. "L'Idée." In his *Idées*. Paris: Draeger, 1948. (Author's translation.)

3. Jane Goodall. "My Life among Wild Chimpanzees." *National Geographic,* vol. 124, 1963, pp. 272–308.

4. A. H. Schultz. "Some Factors Influencing the Social Life of Primates in General and Early Man in Particular." In S. L. Washburn (ed.), *Social Life of Early Man.* New York: Wenner-Gren Foundation for Anthropological Research, Publications in Anthropology, No. 31, 1961, p. 73.

5. George B. Schaller. *The Mountain Gorilla: Ecology and Behavior.* Chicago: University of Chicago Press, 1963.

6. Barbara Harrisson. *Orang-Utan.* New York: Doubleday, 1963.

7. Ashley Montagu. *Darwin, Competition, and Cooperation.* New York: Schuman, 1952.

8. G. A. Bartholomew, Jr., and J. R. Birdsell. "Ecology and the Protohominids." *American Anthropologist,* vol. 55, 1953, pp. 481–498.

9. J. G. Napier. "The Locomotor Functions of Hominids." In S. L. Washburn (ed.), *Classification and Evolution.* New York: Wenner-Gren Foundation for Anthropological Research, Publications in Anthropology, No. 37, 1963, pp. 178–189.

10. H. H. Harlow. "The Evolution of Learning." In Anne Roe and George G. Simpson (eds.), *Behavior and Evolution.* New Haven: Yale University Press, 1958, pp. 269–280.

11. Herbert S. Jennings. *Behavior of the Lower Organisms.* New York: Columbia University Press, 1906. Reprinted by Indiana University Press, Bloomington, 1962.

12. Gaston Viaud. *Intelligence: Its Evolution and Forms.* Translated by A. J. Pomerans. New York: Harper & Row, 1960.

13. Henri Bergson. *Creative Evolution.* Translated by Arthur Mitchell. New York: Holt, 1911.

14. Sir Arthur Keith. *A New Theory of Human Evolution.* London: Watts & Co., 1948, p. 206.

15. L. S. B. Leakey. "Adventures in the Search for Man." *National Geographic,* vol. 123, 1963, pp. 132–152.

16. M. D. Sahlins. "The Social Life of Monkeys, Apes, and Primitive Man." In J. N. Spuhler (ed.), *The Evolution of Man's Capacity for Culture.* Detroit: Wayne State University Press, 1959, pp. 54–73.

17. Raymond A. Dart. "The Gradual Appraisal of *Australopithecus*." In G. Kurth (ed.), *Evolution und Hominisation*. Stuttgart: Fischer, 1962, pp. 141–156.

18. James W. Kitching. *Bone, Tooth & Horn Tools of Palaeolithic Man*. Manchester: Manchester University Press, 1963.

19. Ashley Montagu. *Coming into Being among the Australian Aborigines*. London: Routledge, 1937.

20. D. Aberle *et al.* "The Incest Taboo and the Mating Pattern of Animals." *American Anthropologist*, vol. 65, 1963, pp. 253–265.

21. Ashley Montagu. *The Natural Superiority of Women*. New York: Macmillan, 1953.

22. George D. Stoddard. *The Meaning of Intelligence*. New York: Macmillan, 1943.

23. E. Lloyd DuBrul. *Evolution of the Speech Apparatus*. Springfield, Ill.: C. C. Thomas, 1958; A. L. Bryan. "The Essential Morphological Basis of Human Culture." *Current Anthropology*, vol. 4, 1963, pp. 297–306; C. F. Hockett and R. Ascher. "The Human Revolution." *Current Anthropology*, vol. 5, 1964, pp. 135–168.

24. K. Conrad. "New Problems of Aphasia." *Brain*, vol. 77, 1954, pp. 491–509.

25. Wilder Penfield and Lamar Roberts. *Speech and Brain-Mechanism*. Princeton: Princeton University Press, 1959.

26. Alfred Korzybski. *The Manhood of Humanity*, 2d ed. Lakeville, Conn.: Institute of General Semantics, 1950.

27. Leslie White. "The Concept of Culture." *American Anthropologist*, vol. 61, 1959, pp. 227–251.

28. B. Rensch. "Increase of Learning Capability with Increase of Brain Size." *American Naturalist*, vol. 90, 1956, pp. 81–95.

29. R. W. Gerard. "Brains and Behavior." In Spuhler, *The Evolution of Man's Capacity for Culture*, pp. 14–20.

30. W. Herre. "Einfluss der Umwelt über das Saugetiergehirn." *Deutsche Medizinische Wochenschrift*, vol. 83, 1958, pp. 1568–1574.

31. C. D. Darlington. "The Genetics of Society." In A. J. Gregor (ed.), *A Symposium on Race*. Honolulu: University of Hawaii Press, 1963, pp. 1–36.

32. E. Caspari. "Selective Forces in the Evolution of Man." *American Naturalist*, vol. 97, 1963, pp. 5–14.

33. See Note 5.

34. W. R. Jondorf, R. P. Maichel, and B. B. Brodie. "Inability of Newborn Mice and Guinea Pigs to Metabolize Drugs." *Biochemical Pharmacology*, vol. 1, 1958, pp. 352–354.

35. Clement Smith. *The Physiology of the Newborn Infant*, 3d ed. Springfield, Ill.: C. C. Thomas, 1960.

36. Ashley Montagu. *The Reproductive Development of the Female*. New York: Julian Press, 1957, pp. 166–185.

37. G. J. von Allesch. "Bericht über die drei ersten Lebensmonate eines Schimpansen." *Sitzbericht Preussischen Akademie Wissenschaft*, Berlin (1), 1921, pp. 675–676.

38. Ashley Montagu. "The Mind of the Skin." In his *Anthropology and Human Nature*. New York: McGraw-Hill, 1963, pp. 206–214.

39. Ashley Montagu. *Prenatal Influences*. Springfield, Ill.: C. C. Thomas, 1962, pp. 486–492.

40. Ashley Montagu. *The Direction of Human Development*. New York: Harper & Bros., 1955.

41. Eugene N. Marais. *My Friends the Baboons*. New York: Robert M. McBride, 1940.

42. Robert M. Yerkes and Ada Yerkes. *The Great Apes*. New Haven: Yale University Press, 1929.

43. S. Penbharkkul and S. Karelitz. "Lacrimation in the Neonatal and Early Infancy Period of Premature and Full-Term Infants." *Journal of Pediatrics*, vol. 61, 1963, pp. 859–863.

44. Arthur W. Proetz. *Essays on the Applied Physiology of the Nose*, 2d ed. St. Louis: Annals Publishing Co., 1953.

45. Ashley Montagu. *Darwin, Competition, and Cooperation*. New York: Schuman, 1952.

46. Charles R. Knight. *Prehistoric Man*. New York: Appleton-Century-Crofts, 1949.

47. For the facts, see A. I. Good. "Gorilla-Land." *Natural History*, vol. 56, 1947, pp. 34–46; Albert Schweitzer. *The Animal World of Albert Schweitzer*. Edited by Charles R. Joy. Boston: Beacon, 1959, pp. 97–102; Fred G. Merfield and Harry Miller. *Gorilla Hunter*. New York: Farrar, Straus & Cudahy, 1956; Schaller. *The Mountain Gorilla;* J. E. Pfeiffer. "The Apish Origins of Human Tensions." *Harper's Magazine,* vol. 227, 1963, pp. 55–60; Harrisson. *Orang-Utan;* Goodall. "My Life among Wild Chimpanzees."

48. Raymond A. Dart and Dennis Craig. *Adventures with the Missing Link*. New York: Viking, 1959.

49. Robert Ardrey. *African Genesis*. New York: Atheneum, 1961.

50. Raymond A. Dart. "The Predatory Transition from Ape to Man." *International Anthropological and Linguistic Review*, vol. 1, 1953, pp. 201–208.

51. *Ibid.,* pp. 207–208.

52. For a critical examination by various authors of Golding's thesis, see William Nelson (ed.), *William Golding's Lord of the Flies: A Source Book*. New York: Odyssey, 1963.

53. Robert Ardrey. *The Territorial Imperative*. New York: Atheneum, 1966.

54. François Bourlière. *The Natural History of Animals*. New York: A. A. Knopf, Inc., 1954, pp. 99–100.

55. Barbara Harrisson. *Orang-Utan*. New York: Doubleday, 1963.

56. George Schaller. *The Mountain Gorilla: Ecology and Behavior*. Chicago: University of Chicago Press, 1963, and the same author's *The Year of the Gorilla*. Chicago: University of Chicago Press, 1964.

57. L. L. Bernard. *Instinct.* New York: Holt, 1924; Otto Kline-berg, *Social Psychology.* New York: Holt, 1954, pp. 63–75; David Krech and Richard S. Crutchfield. *Theory and Problems of Social Psychology.* New York: McGraw-Hill, 1948.

58. John Ray. *Collection of English Proverbs.* London, 1670.

59. Friedrich von Bernhardi. *Germany and the Next War.* New York: Longmans, 1912.

60. Konrad Lorenz. *On Aggression.* New York: Harcourt, Brace & World, 1966.

61. See references 3 and 6, and Charles H. Southwick (editor), *Primate Social Behavior.* Princeton, N.J.: Van Nostrand, 1963; Irven DeVore (editor), *Primate Behavior.* New York: Holt, Rine-hart & Winston, 1965; Allan M. Schrier, Harry F. Harlow & Fred Stollnitz (editors), *Behavior of Nonhuman Primates.* 2 vols., New York: Academic Press, 1965.

62. See reference 45.

63. See reference 40.

64. Hugh Miller. *Progress and Decline.* Los Angeles: Anderson & Ritchie, 1963, p. 182.

65. J. E. Pfeiffer. "The Apish Origins of Human Tensions." *Harper's Magazine,* vol. 227, 1963, pp. 55–60.

66. H. Hediger. *Studies of the Psychology and Behaviour of Captive Animals in Zoos and Circuses.* Translated by Geoffrey Sircom. New York: Criterion Books, 1956.

67. Lawrence Kubie. "Instincts and Homeostatis." *Psychoso-matic Medicine,* vol. 10, 1948, pp. 15–30; Ashley Montagu. "Failure of Compensatory Mechanisms in Anxiety." *Journal of Neuropsychiatry,* vol. 5, 1964, pp. 415–417.

68. Otto Rank. *The Trauma of Birth.* New York: Basic Books, 1953.

69. Philip Wheelwright. *The Burning Fountain: A Study in the Language of Symbolism.* Bloomington: Indiana University Press, 1954, p. 366.

70. A. A. Abbie. "A New Approach to Human Evolution." *Transactions of the Royal Society of South Australia,* vol. 75, 1952, pp. 70–88; A. A. Abbie. "Timing in Human Evolution." *Proceedings of the Linnaean Society of New South Wales,* vol. 83, 1958, pp. 197–213.

71. J. N. Spuhler. "Somatic Paths to Culture." In J. N. Spuhler (ed.), *The Evolution of Man's Capacity for Culture,* pp. 4–5.

72. René A. Spitz, *No and Yes: On the Genesis of Human Com-munication.* New York: International Universities Press, 1957.

73. Dudley J. Morton. *The Human Foot.* New York: Hafner, 1949.

74. Hammel, H. T.: "Terrestrial Animals in Cold: Recent Studies of Primitive Man," in *Handbook of Physiology: 4. Adapta-tion to Environment,* D. B. Dill (ed.), Washington, D.C.: Ameri-can Physiological Society, 1964, pp. 413–434.

75. W. Montagna and R. A. Ellis. "New Approaches to the Study of the Skin of Primates." In John Buettner-Janusch (ed.),

Evolutionary and Genetic Biology of Primates, vol. 1. New York: Academic Press, 1963, pp. 179–196.

76. Yas Kuno. *Human Perspiration.* Springfield, Ill.: C. C. Thomas, 1956, p. 340.

77. V. Gordon Childe. *What Happened in History.* Baltimore: Penguin Books, 1963.

78. See Note 40.

79. Petr Kropotkin. *Mutual Aid.* Boston: Porter Sargent, 1955.

80. Roger Caillois. *Man, Play, and Games.* Translated by Meyer Barash. New York: Free Press of Glencoe, 1961.

81. Johan Huizinga. *Homo Ludens: A Study of the Play Element in Culture.* Boston: Beacon, 1955.

82. Kenneth Mather. *Human Diversity.* Edinburgh: Oliver & Boyd, 1964.

83. H. E. L. Mellersh. *The Story of Early Man.* New York: The Viking Press, 1960.

Glossary

Adaptation. A trait of the organism which, in the environment it inhabits, improves its chances of leaving descendants.

Ape. A tailless member of the order Primates, family Pongidae, consisting of the gibbons, orang-utans, chimpanzees, and gorillas.

Apocrine glands. Sweat glands the cells of which contribute part of their protoplasmic substance to their secretion.

Aponeurosis. A fibrous sheet or expanded tendon giving attachment to muscular fibers and serving as the means of origin or insertion of a flat muscle.

Arboreal. Adapted for living in trees.

Australopithecine. A member of the African hominid forms of the Lower Pleistocene or Villafranchian.

Bactericidal. Causing death of bacteria.

Bacteriolytic. Causing dissolution of bacteria.

Bacteriostatic. Inhibiting growth of bacteria.

Brachiation. Progression in trees by swinging by the arms from branches.

Canine teeth. The eye teeth.

Cell. The living acting unit of all plants and animals, consisting of many specialized parts.

Cilia. Hairlike processes of certain cells.

Competition. The process whereby those organisms possessing the adaptive fitness, in the environments they inhabit, are able to leave a larger progeny than those not possessing such fitness. Neither conscious "struggle" nor "survival of the fittest" is implied, but survival of the fit.

Conjunctiva. The mucous membrane covering the anterior surface of the eyeball.

Cortex. The gray matter of the brain.

Cranial capacity. The volume of the interior of the brainbox expressed in cubic centimeters.

Culture. The part of the environment that is learned, shared, and transmitted in society. The man-made part of the environment.

Dolomite. Rock consisting mainly of magnesium carbonate and calcium carbonate.

Dryopithecus. Genus of Miocene apes which may have been ancestral both to the later apes and to man.

Eccrine glands. Sweat glands whose secretion does not involve the removal of any part of the secretory cells.

Ecology. The study of the interactions between organisms and their environment.

Environment. The conditions acting upon the organism.

Enzyme. Substances secreted by the body acting as catalysts causing the chemic processes of the body to be carried on.

Evolution. Development, by descent, with modification.

Fontéchavade. Paleolithic man, known from skull-box of one individual and portion of the forehead bone of another, associated with pre-Mousterian tools (Tayacian). The bones closely resemble those of modern man, and may well be in the vicinity of 100,000 years old or more.

Foramen magnum. The large opening at the base of the skull affording passage to the spinal cord.

Fossil. Remains of an organism or direct evidence of its presence preserved in rocks.

Fronto-occipitalis. The muscle stretching across the top of the head from above the supraorbital line to the back of the head.

Gene. The physical unit of heredity; a small region in a chromosome.

Genetic drift or the Sewall Wright effect. The nonselective random distribution, extinction, or fixation of genes in a population.

Genotype. The genetic constitution, determined by the number, types, and arrangements of genes.

Habitat. The particular kind of environment inhabited by an organism.

Hominid. A member of the genus *Homo*.

Hominidae. The family name of all species of man, including the australopithecines.

Hominoidea. The superfamily including the Hominidae and the Pongidae, i.e., man and the apes.

Homo habilis. Name given to a form of man, at present inadequately described, possibly an advanced australopithecine, perhaps approaching the pithecanthropines. Status at present undetermined.

Homo sapiens. The living species of the genus *Homo*, as well as several extinct forms of this species.

Isolation. The reproductive separation of any two groups or populations.

Kenyapithecus wickeri. A dryopithecine ape from the base of the Pliocene, found at Fort Ternan, Kenya.

Lacrimal. Tear-secreting.

Lysozyme. An enzyme destructive to bacteria.

Mammal. A member of the class of Mammals, characterized by hair, milk secretion, diaphragm used in respiration, lower jaw made up of single pair of bones, and three auditory ossicles in each middle ear connecting eardrum and inner ear.

Masseter muscle. Muscle extending from the zygomatic process of the skull to the ramus and coronoid process of the lower jaw. Its action is to close the jaw.

Mattock. Implement for hacking; adzeshaped, resembling pickax.

Meibomian glands. The sebaceous glands of the eyelids.

Metacarpals. The bones of the hand between the wrist and the fingers.

Metacarpo-phalangeal. The joint between the metacarpals and the finger bones.

Metatarsal. The bones of the foot between the tarsal bones and those of the toes.

Miocene. Geological period of the Tertiary, lasting from about twenty-five to five million years ago.

Monkeys. Primates characterized by tails, comprising the New World Monkeys (Ceboidea) and the Old World Monkeys (Cercopithecoidea).

Morphology. The study of form, usually involving the study of the relation between function, structure, and form.

Mutation. A change in the structure of a gene resulting in a transmissible hereditary modification in the expression of a trait.

Mutation pressure. The measure of the action of mutation in tending to alter the frequency of a gene in a given population.

Nasolacrimal duct. The duct that conducts the fluid from the eye to the nose.

Natural selection. The process whereby those organisms possessing traits that enable them to adapt better to the environment than those lacking the necessary traits are able to leave a larger progeny.

Neanderthal man. Fossil man of Mousterian culture of the Upper Pleistocene.

Neoteny. The developmental retention of fetal or juvenile traits in the adult.

Occipital bone. The bone at the back of the head.

Occlusion. The relation of the upper and lower teeth to each other when the bite is closed or "occluded."

Oligocene. Geological period of the Tertiary, from about thirty-five to twenty-five million years ago.

Order. A systematic category embracing families, genera, species, and their subdivisions, all characterized by a basic pattern of structural traits.

Oreopithecus. An anthropoid genus of the Pliocene.

Paleocene. Geological period of the Tertiary, from seventy-five to fifty-eight million years ago.

Paranthropus. An australopithecine form from South Africa virtually identical with the zinjanthropines of East Africa.

Parietal bones. The two bones of the skull, helping to form its dome and walls, between the frontal and occipital bones (see Fig. 30).

Phenotype. The manifest characteristics of an organism; the product of the joint action of genotype and environment.

Phylogeny. The study of the historical development of the line or lines of evolution in a group of organisms.

Pithecanthropine. Resembling *Homo erectus*.

Pithecanthropus. Preferably known as *Homo erectus*, extinct form of man of Middle Pleistocene age.

Pleistocene. The first Epoch of the Quaternary, characterized by the rise and recession of the continental ice sheets. The Age of Man.

Pluvial. A rainy period.

Pongidae. The family of apes, usually omitting the gibbons, and including the orang-utan, the chimpanzee, and the gorilla.

Population. The group of individuals which forms a single interbreeding community.

Potassium-Argon dating. A method of determining the age of fossils by measuring the transformation of potassium into argon.

Preadaptation. Not really different in meaning from *Adaptation,* but usually taken to mean the reapplication of structures or functions to life in a new environment.

Primate. A member of the order Primates, consisting of the lemurs, lorises, tarsiers, monkeys, apes, and men.

Proconsul. An apelike fossil form from the Lower Miocene of East Africa.

Prognathism. Anterior projection of the jaws.

Proprioception. The reception of stimuli originating in the muscles, tendons, and other internal tissues.

Pterygoid muscles. Muscles acting to bring the lower jaw forward and upward.

Sagittal crest. The plate of bone, in some primates, running in an anteroposterior direction across the top of the skull, and giving attachment to the temporal muscles.

Savanna. A grassland characterized by scattered trees, especially in tropical and subtropical regions; a cross between a woodland and a desert.

Selection. The maintenance of certain genetic constitutions (genotypes) having adaptive value in contrast with others that do not, and which are therefore not likely to do as well by way of leaving progeny.

Selection pressure. The measure of the action of selection in tending to alter the frequency of a gene in a given population.

Simian gap. The premaxillary diastema, a space situated between the upper lateral incisor and the upper canine on each side of the jaw, serving to accommodate the lower canine, in most primates.

Sinanthropus. Now preferably known as *Homo erectus pekinensis,* fossil hominid of Middle Pleistocene age, found at Choukoutien, S. W. of Peking, China.

Skull. The bony framework of the head (see Figs. 30 and 31).

Social selection. Selection on the basis of some socially preferred trait or traits.

Specialization. The development of special adaptations to a particular habitat or mode of life.

Species. A group of actually or potentially interbreeding natural populations, which is more or less reproductively isolated from other such groups.

Suture. The edges at which the different bones of the skull come together, and with age unite.

Talus. The ankle bone, the bone of the foot that articulates with the tibia and fibula to form the ankle joint.

Temporal muscles. The muscles originating on the walls of the skull and inserting on the rami of the lower jaw. Their action is to close the jaw.

Tibia. The shinbone.

Villafranchian. The earliest part of the Pleistocene before the first glaciation (Günz).

Zinjanthropus. An australopithecine of Lower Pleistocene age, from East Africa.

Zygomatic arches. The arches forming part of the cheek bones.

Index